# HUNSLET
# NARROW GAUGE
# LOCOMOTIVES

## ANDREW NEALE

PLATEWAY PRESS

# PUBLISHER'S PREFACE

This reprint consists of a selection from the individual catalogue sheets that were published by the Hunslet Engine Co. Ltd. to describe their various steam and diesel locomotives. Only narrow gauge locomotives of 1ft 6in to 3ft 6in gauge have been included. Amongst these are three sheets illustrating Avonside and Kerr Stuart steam locomotives as these designs were included in the Hunslet range following the acquisition of those companies' drawings, patterns and goodwill. An appendix has been added to identify the particular locomotives illustrated.

Grateful thanks are due to Messrs. Geoff Horsman and Peter Halton for their assistance with certain historical details and to Roy Link for cover artwork and book design.

ANDREW NEALE, Editor.

© Plateway Press 1995 (new material)

Reprinted May 2000

ISBN 1 871980 28 3

Printed by Postprint
Taverner House, Harling Road, East Harling, Norfolk  NR16 2QR, UK


PLATEWAY PRESS
Taverner House, Harling Road, East Harling, Norfolk  NR16 2QR, UK

# INTRODUCTION

The parish of Hunslet, a district on the south side of the Yorkshire city of Leeds has become a familiar name throughout the railways of the world. Thanks to the pioneering work of Matthew Murray, Leeds can justifiably claim to rival Newcastle as the birthplace of the steam locomotive. But it is the name Hunslet, as embodied by the formation of the Hunslet Engine Co. in 1864, which has carried the fame of Leeds around the world on the thousands of steam and diesel locomotives that have been built at Leeds since that date.

The founder of the Hunslet Engine Company was John Towlerton Leather, a well known civil engineering contractor. The works was established on the site of the famous Railway Foundry of E. B. Wilson & Co., and surrounded by three other locomotive builders – Kitson & Co., Hudswell Clarke, and Manning Wardle – all whom were destined to become associated with the Hunslet Engine Co. Despite this close proximity, the industrial steam locomotive market was then so buoyant that there was a fair degree of friendly co-operation between them rather fierce competition.

At this time the industrial steam locomotive was just becoming an essential part of a civil engineering contractor's plant so it is not surprising that Hunslet's earliest customers were well known names within that industry. The first locomotive built was LINDEN, a standard gauge 0-6-0 saddletank with 14in x 18in inside cylinders and 3ft 4in diameter wheels delivered to Brassey & Ballard at Ampthill, Beds. on 18 July 1865 for work on the Midland Railway's London extension. A second identical locomotive was built for the Waterloo Main colliery in Leeds in October and other early customers included contractors such as Peto & Betts, J. T. Firbank and Waring Brothers.

Export business began as early as May 1866 when an 0-4-0 saddletank was shipped to Java whilst the first narrow gauge locomotive was completed in 1870. Significantly this was a 1ft 10¾ in gauge cabless 0-4-0ST for Dinorwic slate quarry in North Wales. Over the years it is the large number of these 'Hunslet Quarry Tanks', together with the famous 'Austerity' 0-6-0 saddle tank developed during World War II, that have made the name of Hunslet so well known to railway enthusiasts.

The first three foot gauge gauge locomotives, a pair of four coupled saddletanks for reservoir construction work, quickly followed and by 1902 the company had built to a wide variety of gauges between 18 inches and four feet. This variation in gauge is partly accounted for by the various metric gauges that exported locomotives were built to, but primarily due to the numerous gauges in use in Britain. Many locomotives were built over the years for the Irish three foot gauge lines but locos built for British industrial concerns included ones to such odd gauges as 2ft 8in, 2ft 9in and 3ft 4in.

Like the rest of the railway industry, Hunslet's 'golden age' was the period prior to the World War I. During this time a tremendous variety of locomotives were built, including many tank and tender locomotives for public railways overseas. Average annual output was thirty-one locomotives but production fell during the World War I, with many staff called up and much of the works turned over to armaments and other government work. Locomotive production continued, however, notably with the building of 155 'War Office' class 4-6-0 side tanks for the 60cm gauge military light railways.

The post first war period was a difficult one, with economic slump causing the closure of many locomotive builders, including Manning Wardle who ceased work in 1927. Of more significance to Hunslet were the closures of Kerr Stuart in 1930 and the Avonside Engine Co. in 1935 for in each case Hunslet subsequently acquired their drawings, patterns and good will. Both firms had a well–established range of industrial steam locomotives and Hunslet built many more engines to these designs. These included two Avonside pattern 2ft 6in gauge 0-6-2 side tanks for Nepal as late as 1962 and the final steam locomotive of all, a Kerr Stuart 'Brazil' class 750mm gauge 0-4-2 saddletank for Java in 1971.

Diesel locomotive production commenced in 1931 with a standard gauge 0-6-0, and the acquisition of Kerr Stuart and Avonside gave access to much needed design knowledge and experience. The well known 'Hudson-Hunslet' range of small narrow gauge diesels were directly developed from the earlier Kerr Stuart range whilst Avonside's experience in building articulated diesel and steam locomotives proved most useful.

Hunslet went on to develop some very large diesel locomotives for main line use but their greatest contribution to diesel locomotive development was the production of a practical flame proofed narrow gauge machine for underground use in collieries and other mines. The pioneer 2ft gauge 25 h.p. locos were built in 1939 and after World War II the range was quickly improved and extended. Four and six coupled machines of up to 100 h.p. were developed for both coal hauling and man riding work, followed later by 'double-ended' machines. More recently a unique rack railed mining loco has been developed as well as more conventional large Bo-Bo machines for the long hauls often found in modern pits.

The company continued to flourish throughout the 1970's and 80's, the locomotive range of neighbours Hudswell Clarke being absorbed in 1972. More recently much work has been undertaken for British Rail as well as for traditional customers at home and abroad. Sadly the continuing general decline of the railway industry and a number of changes in the company's ownership have contributed to a sharp decline in Hunslet's fortunes. At the time of writing (September 1995) it is uncertain if the company will survive – at least in Leeds – to see in the millennium.

## 0-6-4 TYPE

# SADDLE TANK ENGINE

| | |
|---|---|
| Gauge of Railway ... ... ... ... ... ... ... ... | 1 ft. 11¼ in. |
| Size of Cylinders ... ... ... ... ... ... ... ... | 10 in. dia. × 16 in. stroke |
| Dia. of Coupled Wheels ... ... ... ... ... ... ... | 2 ft. 6 in. |
| ,, Bogie Wheels ... ... ... ... ... ... ... | 1 ,, 10 ,, |
| Rigid Wheelbase (Engine) ... ... ... ... ... ... | 6 ,, 2 ,, |
| Total Wheelbase (Engine) ... ... ... ... ... ... | 15 ,, 11 ,, |
| Height from Rail to Top of Chimney ... ... ... ... | 8 ,, 10½ ,, |
| Extreme Width ... ... ... ... ... ... ... ... | 6 ,, 4 ,, |
| Heating Surface—Small Tubes ... ... ... ... 377 sq. ft. | |
| ,, ,, Firebox ... ... ... ... 39 ,, | |
| Total ... ... ... 416 ,, ... | 416 sq. ft. |
| Grate Area ... ... ... ... ... ... ... ... | 7·5 ,, |
| Working Pressure ... ... ... ... ... ... ... | 120 lbs. per sq. in. |
| Tank Capacity ... ... ... ... ... ... ... | 450 gallons |
| Fuel Space (Coal) ... ... ... ... ... ... ... | 13 cwts. |
| Weight Empty (Engine) ... ... ... ... ... ... | 14 tons 10 cwts. |
| ,, in Working Order (Engine) ... ... ... ... ... | 17 ,, 0 ,, |
| Tractive Effort at 75 per cent. of Boiler Pressure ... ... ... ... | 4800 lbs. |
| Minimum Radius of Curve Engine will traverse with ease ... .. | 300 ft. |
| Weight per Yard of Lightest Rail advisable ... ... ... .. | 20 lbs. |
| Load Engine will haul on Level ... ... ... ... ... .. | 250 tons |
| ,, ,, ,, up Incline of 1 in 100 ... ... ... .. | 120 ,, |
| ,, ,, ,, ,, ,, 1 in 50 ... ... ... .. | 65 ,, |

*Code Word*—**BEDERT**

## 4-4-0 TYPE

# TENDER ENGINE

| | | |
|---|---|---|
| Gauge of Railway | | 3 ft. 0 in. |
| Size of Cylinders | | 12 in. dia. × 16 in. stroke |
| Dia. of Coupled Wheels | | 3 ft. 2 in. |
| ,, Bogie Wheels | | 1 ,, 10½ ,, |
| ,, Tender Wheels | | 2 ,, 9 ,, |
| Rigid Wheelbase (Engine) | | 7 ,, 0 ,, |
| Total Wheelbase (Engine) | | 17 ,, 3 ,, |
| ,, ,, (Engine and Tender) | | 31 ,, 3¾ ,, |
| Height from Rail to Top of Chimney | | 12 ,, 2¾ ,, |
| Extreme Width | | 7 ,, 7¼ ,, |
| Heating Surface—Small Tubes | 393 sq. ft. | |
| ,, ,, Firebox | 57 ,, | |
| Total | 450 ,, | 450 sq. ft. |
| Grate Area | | 8 ,, |
| Working Pressure | | 130 lbs. per sq. in. |
| Tank Capacity | | 1029 gallons |
| Fuel Space (Wood) | | 1 ton 14 cwts. |
| Weight Empty (Engine) | | 16 tons 10 ,, |
| ,, ,, (Tender) | | 7 ,, 15 ,, |
| Weight in Working Order (Engine) | | 18 ,, 0 ,, |
| ,, ,, ,, (Tender) | | 13 ,, 10 ,, |
| Total Weight of Engine and Tender in Working Order | | 31 ,, 10 ,, |
| Tractive Effort at 75 per cent. of Boiler Pressure | | 5911 lbs. |
| Minimum Radius of Curve Engine will traverse with ease | | 320 ft. |
| Weight per Yard of Lightest Rail advisable | | 40 lbs. |
| Load Engine will haul on Level | | 295 tons |
| ,, ,, ,, up Incline of 1 in 100 | | 140 ,, |
| ,, ,, ,, ,, ,, 1 in 50 | | 70 ,, |

*Code Word*—**MURTA**

## 0-4-0 TYPE

# SADDLE TANK ENGINE

| | |
|---|---|
| Gauge of Railway ... ... ... ... ... ... ... ... | 3 ft. 0 in. |
| Size of Cylinders ... ... ... ... ... ... ... ... ... | 6 in. dia. × 10 in. stroke |
| Dia. of Coupled Wheels ... ... ... ... ... ... ... | 1 ft. 8 in. |
| Rigid Wheelbase (Engine) ... ... ... ... ... ... | 3 ,, 3 ,, |
| Height from Rail to Top of Chimney ... ... ... ... | 8 ,, 5 ,, |
| Extreme Width ... ... ... ... ... ... ... ... | 5 ,, 0 ,, |
| Heating Surface—Small Tubes ... ... ... 94 sq. ft. | |
| ,, ,, Firebox ... ... ... 15 ,, | |
| Total ... ... ... 109 ,, ... | 109 sq. ft. |
| Grate Area ... ... ... ... ... ... ... ... | 2·5 ,, |
| Working Pressure ... ... ... ... ... ... ... | 120 lbs. per sq. in. |
| Tank Capacity ... ... ... ... ... ... ... ... | 100 gallons |
| Fuel Space (Coal) ... ... ... ... ... ... ... | 2 cwts. |
| Weight Empty (Engine) ... ... ... ... ... ... | 5 tons 10 cwts. |
| ,, in Working Order (Engine) ... ... ... ... ... | 6 ,, 7 ,, |
| Total Weight on Coupled Wheels ... ... ... ... ... | 6 ,, 7 ,, |
| Tractive Effort at 75 per cent. of Boiler Pressure ... ... ... ... | 1620 lbs. |
| Ratio Adhesive Weight ÷ Tractive Effort ... ... ... ... ... | 8·8 |
| Minimum Radius of Curve Engine will traverse with ease ... ... ... | 21 ft. |
| Weight per Yard of Lightest Rail advisable ... ... ... ... | 20 lbs. |
| Load Engine will haul on Level ... ... ... ... ... ... | 80 tons |
| ,, ,, ,, up Incline of 1 in 100 ... ... ... ... | 40 ,, |
| ,, ,, ,, ,, ,, 1 in 50 ... ... ... ... | 20 ,, |

*Code Word*—**CHAMP**

## 0-4-0  TYPE

# SADDLE  TANK  ENGINE

| | |
|---|---|
| Gauge of Railway | 2 ft.  1¾₁₆ in. |
| Size of Cylinders | 7 in. dia. × 10 in. stroke |
| Dia. of Coupled Wheels | 1 ft.  8  in. |
| Rigid Wheelbase (Engine) | 3  ,,  3  ,, |
| Height from Rail to Top of Chimney | 8  ,,  3¼  ,, |
| Extreme Width | 5  ,,  8  ,, |
| Heating Surface—Small Tubes | 86 sq. ft. |
| ,,       ,,       Firebox | 14   ,, |
| Total | 100   ,,       100 sq. ft. |
| Grate Area | 2·5   ,, |
| Working Pressure | 120 lbs. per sq. in. |
| Tank Capacity | 130 gallons |
| Fuel Space | 2 cwts. |
| Weight Empty (Engine) | 5 tons 15 cwts. |
| ,,  in Working Order (Engine) | 6  ,,  12  ,, |
| Total Weight on Coupled Wheels | 6  ,,  12  ,, |
| Tractive Effort at 75 per cent. of Boiler Pressure | 2205 lbs. |
| Ratio Adhesive Weight ÷ Tractive Effort | 6·7 |
| Minimum Radius of Curve Engine will traverse with ease | 21 ft. |
| Weight per Yard of Lightest Rail advisable | 20 lbs. |
| Load Engine will haul on Level | 115 tons |
| ,,       ,,       ,,  up Incline of 1 in 100 | 55  ,, |
| ,,       ,,       ,,       ,,       ,,  1 in 50 | 30  ,, |

*Code Word*—HELVA

## 0-4-0 TYPE

# SADDLE TANK ENGINE

| | |
|---|---|
| Gauge of Railway ... ... ... ... ... ... ... ... | 3 ft. 6 in. |
| Size of Cylinders ... ... ... ... ... ... ... ... | 7½ in. dia. × 12 in. stroke |
| Dia. of Coupled Wheels ... ... ... ... ... ... ... | 2 ft. 2 in. |
| Rigid Wheelbase (Engine) ... ... ... ... ... ... | 4 ,, 3 ,, |
| Height from Rail to Top of Chimney ... ... ... ... | 9 ,, 0 ,, |
| Extreme Width ... ... ... ... ... ... ... ... | 6 ,, 0 ,, |
| Heating Surface—Small Tubes ... ... ... ... 108 sq. ft. | |
| ,, ,, Firebox ... ... ... 18 ,, | |
| Total ... ... ... 126 ,, ... | 126 sq. ft. |
| Grate Area ... ... ... ... ... ... ... ... | 3 ,, |
| Working Pressure ... ... ... ... ... ... ... | 130 lbs. per sq. in. |
| Tank Capacity ... ... ... ... ... ... ... ... | 200 gallons |
| Fuel Space (Coal) ... ... ... ... ... ... ... | 5 cwts. |
| Weight Empty (Engine) ... ... ... ... ... ... | 7 tons 5 cwts. |
| ,, in Working Order (Engine) ... ... ... ... | 8 ,, 10 ,, |
| Total Weight on Coupled Wheels ... ... ... ... ... | 8 ,, 10 ,, |
| Tractive Effort at 75 per cent. of Boiler Pressure ... ... ... | 2534 lbs. |
| Ratio Adhesive Weight ÷ Tractive Effort ... ... ... ... | 7·3 |
| Minimum Radius of Curve Engine will traverse with ease ... ... | 36 ft. |
| Weight per Yard of Lightest Rail advisable ... ... ... | 25 lbs. |
| Load Engine will haul on Level ... ... ... ... ... | 130 tons |
| ,, ,, ,, up Incline of 1 in 100 ... ... ... ... | 65 ,, |
| ,, ,, ,, ,, ,, 1 in 50 ... ... ... ... | 35 ,, |

*Code Word*—**SANTAL**

## 0-6-0 TYPE

# SIDE TANK ENGINE

| | |
|---|---|
| Gauge of Railway ... ... ... ... ... ... ... ... | 3 ft. 3⅜ in. |
| Size of Cylinders ... ... ... ... ... ... ... ... ... | 8 in. dia. × 12 in. stroke |
| Dia. of Coupled Wheels ... ... ... ... ... ... ... | 2 ft. 6 in. |
| Rigid Wheelbase (Engine) ... ... ... ... ... ... | 7 ,, 8 ,, |
| Height from Rail to Top of Chimney ... ... ... ... | 9 ,, 9 ,, |
| Extreme Width ... ... ... ... ... ... ... ... | 7 ,, 1 ,, |
| Heating Surface—Small Tubes ... ... ... ... 146 sq. ft. | |
| ,, ,, Firebox ... ... ... ... 20 ,, | |
| Total ... ... ... 166 ,, ... | 166 sq. ft. |
| Grate Area ... ... ... ... ... ... ... ... | 3·25 ,, |
| Working Pressure ... ... ... ... ... ... ... | 140 lbs. per sq. in. |
| Tank Capacity ... ... ... ... ... ... ... ... | 300 gallons |
| Fuel Space (Coal) ... ... ... ... ... ... ... | 11 cwts. |
| Weight Empty (Engine) ... ... ... ... ... ... | 10 tons 1 cwts. |
| ,, in Working Order (Engine) ... ... ... ... | 12 ,, 9 ,, |
| Total Weight on Coupled Wheels ... ... ... ... | 12 ,, 9 ,, |
| Tractive Effort at 75 per cent. of Boiler Pressure ... ... ... ... | 2688 lbs. |
| Ratio Adhesive Weight ÷ Tractive Effort ... ... ... ... | 10 |
| Minimum Radius of Curve Engine will traverse with ease ... ... | 138 ft. |
| Weight per Yard of Lightest Rail advisable ... ... ... | 20 lbs. |
| Load Engine will haul on Level ... ... ... ... ... | 135 tons |
| ,, ,, ,, up Incline of 1 in 100 ... ... ... ... | 65 ,, |
| ,, ,, ,, ,, ,, 1 in 50 ... ... ... ... | 35 ,, |

*Code Word—***ABEJA**

## 0-6-0 TYPE
# SIDE TANK ENGINE

| | |
|---|---|
| Gauge of Railway ... ... ... ... ... ... ... ... | 3 ft. 3¾ in. |
| Size of Cylinders ... ... ... ... ... ... ... ... | 9 in. dia. × 14 in. stroke |
| Dia. of Coupled Wheels ... ... ... ... ... ... ... | 2 ft. 9 in. |
| Rigid Wheelbase (Engine) ... ... ... ... ... ... | 7 ,, 0 ,, |
| Height from Rail to Top of Chimney ... ... ... ... | 10 ,, 3½ ,, |
| Extreme Width ... ... ... ... ... ... ... ... | 6 ,, 6¾ ,, |
| Heating Surface—Small Tubes ... ... ... ... 205 sq. ft. | |
| ,, ,, Firebox ... ... ... ... 30 ,, | |
| Total ... ... ... 235 ,, ... | 235 sq. ft. |
| Grate Area ... ... ... ... ... ... ... ... | 4·25 ,, |
| Working Pressure ... ... ... ... ... ... ... | 140 lbs. per sq. in. |
| Tank Capacity ... ... ... ... ... ... ... ... | 300 gallons |
| Fuel Space (Coal) ... ... ... ... ... ... ... | 18 cwts. |
| Weight Empty (Engine) ... ... ... ... ... ... | 11 tons 15 cwts. |
| ,, in Working Order (Engine) ... ... ... ... | 14 ,, 19 ,, |
| Total Weight on Coupled Wheels ... ... ... ... ... | 14 ,, 19 ,, |
| Maximum Axle Load ... ... ... ... ... ... ... | 5 ,, 19 ,, |
| Tractive Effort at 75 per cent. of Boiler Pressure ... ... ... | 3608 lbs. |
| Ratio Adhesive Weight ÷ Tractive Effort ... ... ... ... ... | 9·3 |
| Minimum Radius of Curve Engine will traverse with ease ... ... | 98 ft. |
| Weight per Yard of Lightest Rail advisable ... ... ... ... | 30 lbs. |
| Load Engine will haul on Level ... ... ... ... ... | 185 tons |
| ,, ,, ,, up Incline of 1 in 100 ... ... ... | 90 ,, |
| ,, ,, ,, ,, ,, 1 in 50 ... ... ... ... | 45 ,, |

*Code Word*—**RAFLA**

## 0-4-2 TYPE
# SIDE TANK ENGINE

| | |
|---|---|
| Gauge of Railway ... ... ... ... ... ... ... ... | 3 ft. 6 in. |
| Size of Cylinders ... ... ... ... ... ... ... ... | 7 in. dia. × 12 in. stroke |
| Dia. of Coupled Wheels ... ... ... ... ... ... ... | 2 ft. 0 in. |
| ,, Bogie Wheels ... ... ... ... ... ... | 1 ,, 6½ ,, |
| Rigid Wheelbase (Engine) ... ... ... ... ... | 3 ,, 6 ,, |
| Total Wheelbase (Engine) ... ... ... ... ... | 7 ,, 9 ,, |
| Height from Rail to Top of Chimney ... ... ... | 9 ,, 0 ,, |
| Extreme Width ... ... ... ... ... ... ... ... | 6 ,, 1½ ,, |
| Heating Surface—Small Tubes ... ... ... ... 127 sq. ft. | |
| ,, ,, Firebox ... ... ... ... 21 ,, | |
| Total ... ... ... 148 ,, | 148 sq. ft. |
| Grate Area ... ... ... ... ... ... ... ... | 3·5 ,, |
| Working Pressure ... ... ... ... ... ... ... | 160 lbs. per sq. in. |
| Tank Capacity ... ... ... ... ... ... ... | 200 gallons |
| Fuel Space (Wood) ... ... ... ... ... ... | 3¾ cwts. |
| Weight Empty (Engine) ... ... ... ... ... | 8 tons 10 cwts. |
| ,, in Working Order (Engine) ... ... ... ... | 9 ,, 17 ,, |
| Total Weight on Coupled Wheels ... ... ... ... | 7 ,, 9 ,, |
| Maximum Axle Load ... ... ... ... ... ... | 4 ,, 5 ,, |
| Tractive Effort at 75 per cent. of Boiler Pressure ... ... ... | 2940 lbs. |
| Ratio Adhesive Weight ÷ Tractive Effort ... ... ... ... | 5·7 |
| Minimum Radius of Curve Engine will traverse with ease ... ... | 95 ft. |
| Weight per Yard of Lightest Rail advisable ... ... ... ... | 25 lbs. |
| Load Engine will haul on Level ... ... ... ... ... ... | 150 tons |
| ,, ,, ,, up Incline of 1 in 100 ... ... ... ... | 75 ,, |
| ,, ,, ,, ,, ,, 1 in 50 ... ... ... ... | 40 ,, |

*Code Word*—**DRYBRO**

# THE HUNSLET ENGINE CO. LTD *Engineers* LEEDS ENGLAND

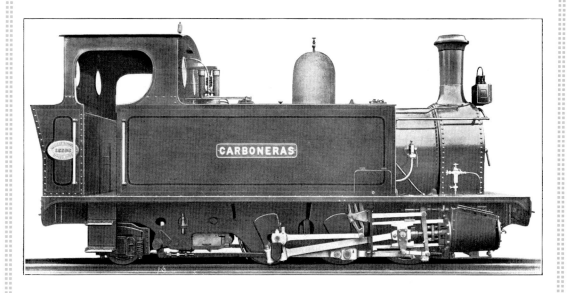

## 0-6-2 TYPE
# SIDE TANK ENGINE

| | |
|---|---|
| Gauge of Railway ... ... ... ... ... ... ... ... | 2 ft. 6 in. |
| Size of Cylinders ... ... ... ... ... ... ... ... | 13 in. dia. × 16 in. stroke |
| Dia. of Coupled Wheels ... ... ... ... ... ... ... | 2 ft. 6 in. |
| ,, Bogie Wheels ... ... ... ... ... ... ... | 1 ,, 8 ,, |
| Rigid Wheelbase (Engine) ... ... ... ... ... ... | 6 ,, 0 ,, |
| Total Wheelbase (Engine) ... ... ... ... ... ... | 12 ,, 6 ,, |
| Height from Rail to Top of Chimney ... ... ... ... | 10 ,, 0 ,, |
| Extreme Width ... ... ... ... ... ... ... ... | 8 ,, 4⅝ ,, |
| Heating Surface—Small Tubes ... ... ... ... 500 sq. ft. | |
| ,, ,, Firebox ... ... ... 45 ,, | |
| Total ... ... ... 545 ,, ... | 545 sq. ft. |
| Grate Area ... ... ... ... ... ... ... ... | 8·3 ,, |
| Working Pressure ... ... ... ... ... ... ... | 150 lbs. per sq. in. |
| Tank Capacity ... ... ... ... ... ... ... ... | 750 gallons |
| Fuel Space (Coal) ... ... ... ... ... ... ... | 1 ton 0 cwts. |
| Weight Empty (Engine) ... ... ... ... ... ... | 19 tons 15 ,, |
| ,, in Working Order (Engine) ... ... ... ... ... | 24 ,, 5 ,, |
| Total Weight on Coupled Wheels ... ... ... ... ... | 17 ,, 13 ,, |
| Maximum Axle Load ... ... ... ... ... ... ... | 6 ,, 1 ,, |
| Tractive Effort at 75 per cent. of Boiler Pressure ... ... ... | 10140 lbs. |
| Ratio Adhesive Weight ÷ Tractive Effort ... ... ... ... | 3·9 |
| Minimum Radius of Curve Engine will traverse with ease ... ... | 200 ft. |
| Weight per Yard of Lightest Rail advisable ... ... ... ... | 30 lbs. |
| Load Engine will haul on Level ... ... ... ... ... | 540 tons |
| ,, ,, ,, up Incline of 1 in 100 ... ... ... ... | 275 ,, |
| ,, ,, ,, ,, ,, 1 in 50 ... ... ... ... | 155 ,, |

*Code Word*—**CARBO**

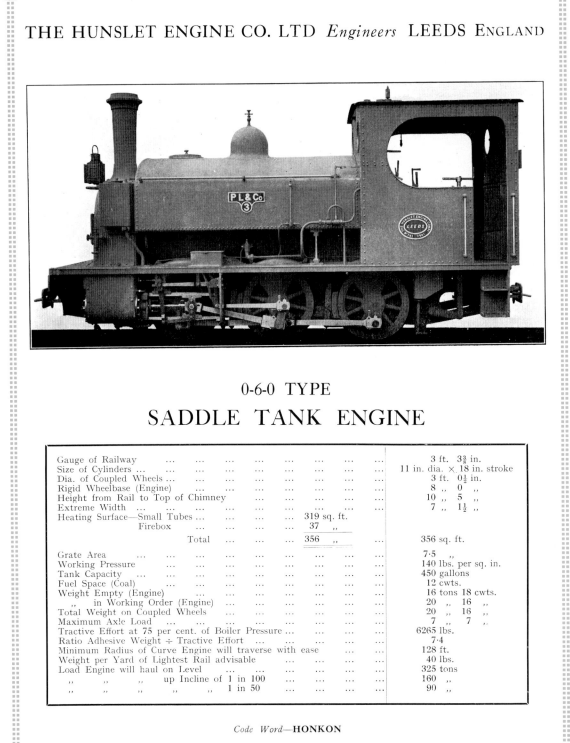

## 0-6-0 TYPE

# SADDLE TANK ENGINE

| | |
|---|---|
| Gauge of Railway ... ... ... ... ... ... ... ... | 3 ft. 3⅜ in. |
| Size of Cylinders ... ... ... ... ... ... ... ... | 11 in. dia. × 18 in. stroke |
| Dia. of Coupled Wheels ... ... ... ... ... ... ... | 3 ft. 0½ in. |
| Rigid Wheelbase (Engine) ... ... ... ... ... ... | 8 ,, 0 ,, |
| Height from Rail to Top of Chimney ... ... ... ... | 10 ,, 5 ,, |
| Extreme Width ... ... ... ... ... ... ... ... | 7 ,, 1½ ,, |
| Heating Surface—Small Tubes ... ... ... ... 319 sq. ft. | |
| Firebox ... ... ... ... 37 ,, | |
| Total ... ... ... 356 ,, ... | 356 sq. ft. |
| Grate Area ... ... ... ... ... ... ... ... | 7·5 ,, |
| Working Pressure ... ... ... ... ... ... ... | 140 lbs. per sq. in. |
| Tank Capacity ... ... ... ... ... ... ... ... | 450 gallons |
| Fuel Space (Coal) ... ... ... ... ... ... ... | 12 cwts. |
| Weight Empty (Engine) ... ... ... ... ... ... | 16 tons 18 cwts. |
| ,, in Working Order (Engine) ... ... ... ... | 20 ,, 16 ,, |
| Total Weight on Coupled Wheels ... ... ... ... | 20 ,, 16 ,, |
| Maximum Axle Load ... ... ... ... ... ... | 7 ,, 7 ,, |
| Tractive Effort at 75 per cent. of Boiler Pressure ... ... ... | 6265 lbs. |
| Ratio Adhesive Weight ÷ Tractive Effort ... ... ... ... | 7·4 |
| Minimum Radius of Curve Engine will traverse with ease ... ... | 128 ft. |
| Weight per Yard of Lightest Rail advisable ... ... ... | 40 lbs. |
| Load Engine will haul on Level ... ... ... ... ... | 325 tons |
| ,, ,, ,, up Incline of 1 in 100 ... ... ... ... | 160 ,, |
| ,, ,, ,, ,, ,, 1 in 50 ... ... ... ... | 90 ,, |

*Code Word—***HONKON**

# THE HUNSLET ENGINE CO. LTD *Engineers* LEEDS ENGLAND

## 0-6-0 TYPE

# SIDE TANK ENGINE

| | |
|---|---|
| Gauge of Railway ... ... ... ... ... ... ... ... | 3 ft. 3¾ in. |
| Size of Cylinders ... ... ... ... ... ... ... ... | 13 in. dia. × 18 in. stroke |
| Dia. of Coupled Wheels ... ... ... ... ... ... ... | 3 ft. 3 in. |
| Rigid Wheelbase (Engine) ... ... ... ... ... ... | 11 ,, 0 ,, |
| Height from Rail to Top of Chimney ... ... ... | 11 ,, 0 ,, |
| Extreme Width ... ... ... ... ... ... ... ... | 8 ,, 0½ ,, |
| Heating Surface—Small Tubes ... ... ... ... 500 sq. ft. | |
| ,, ,, Firebox ... ... ... ... 65 ,, | |
| Total ... ... ... 565 ,, ... | 565 sq. ft. |
| Grate Area ... ... ... ... ... ... ... ... | 9·5 ,, |
| Working Pressure ... ... ... ... ... ... ... | 160 lbs. per sq. in. |
| Tank Capacity ... ... ... ... ... ... ... ... | 620 gallons |
| Fuel Space (Coal) ... ... ... ... ... ... ... | 1 ton 0 cwts. |
| Weight Empty (Engine) ... ... ... ... ... ... | 21 tons 11 ,, |
| ,, in Working Order (Engine) ... ... ... ... | 26 ,, 11 ,, |
| Total Weight on Coupled Wheels ... ... ... ... | 26 ,, 11 ,, |
| Maximum Axle Load ... ... ... ... ... ... | 9 ,, 0 ,, |
| Tractive Effort at 75 per cent. of Boiler Pressure ... ... ... | 9360 lbs. |
| Ratio Adhesive Weight ÷ Tractive Effort ... ... ... ... | 6·3 |
| Minimum Radius of Curve Engine will traverse with ease ... ... | 242 ft. |
| Weight per Yard of Lightest Rail advisable ... ... ... ... | 45 lbs. |
| Load Engine will haul on Level ... ... ... ... ... | 490 tons |
| ,, ,, ,, up Incline of 1 in 100 ... ... ... ... | 245 ,, |
| ,, ,, ,, ,, ,, 1 in 50 ... ... ... ... | 135 ,, |

*Code Word—***NALON**

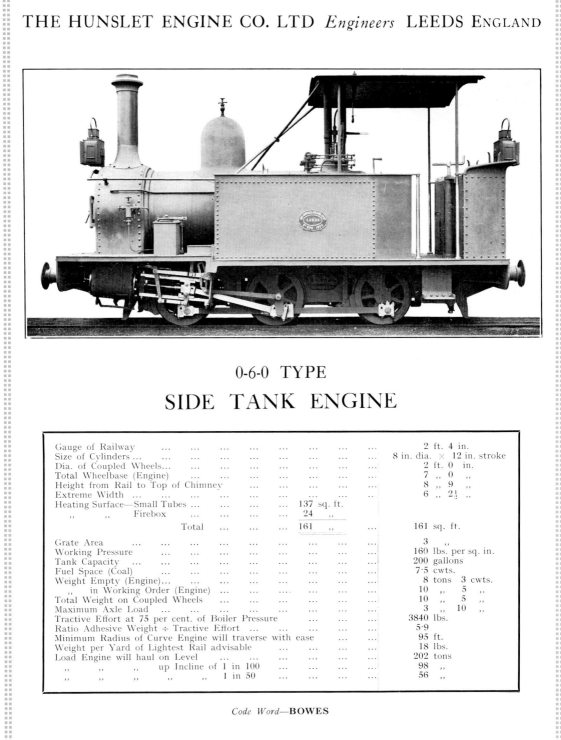

## 0-6-0 TYPE

# SIDE TANK ENGINE

| | |
|---|---|
| Gauge of Railway ... ... ... ... ... ... ... ... | 2 ft. 4 in. |
| Size of Cylinders ... ... ... ... ... ... ... ... | 8 in. dia. × 12 in. stroke |
| Dia. of Coupled Wheels... ... ... ... ... ... ... | 2 ft. 0 in. |
| Total Wheelbase (Engine) ... ... ... ... ... ... | 7 ,, 0 ,, |
| Height from Rail to Top of Chimney ... ... ... ... | 8 ,, 9 ,, |
| Extreme Width ... ... ... ... ... ... ... | 6 ,, 2½ ,, |
| Heating Surface—Small Tubes ... ... ... ... 137 sq. ft. | |
| ,, ,, Firebox ... ... ... ... 24 ,, | |
| Total ... ... ... 161 ,, ... | 161 sq. ft. |
| Grate Area ... ... ... ... ... ... ... ... | 3 ,, |
| Working Pressure ... ... ... ... ... ... ... | 160 lbs. per sq. in. |
| Tank Capacity ... ... ... ... ... ... ... ... | 200 gallons |
| Fuel Space (Coal) ... ... ... ... ... ... ... | 7·5 cwts. |
| Weight Empty (Engine)... ... ... ... ... ... ... | 8 tons 3 cwts. |
| ,, in Working Order (Engine) ... ... ... ... | 10 ,, 5 ,, |
| Total Weight on Coupled Wheels ... ... ... ... | 10 ,, 5 ,, |
| Maximum Axle Load ... ... ... ... ... ... | 3 ,, 10 ,, |
| Tractive Effort at 75 per cent. of Boiler Pressure ... ... ... | 3840 lbs. |
| Ratio Adhesive Weight ÷ Tractive Effort ... ... ... ... | 5·9 |
| Minimum Radius of Curve Engine will traverse with ease ... ... | 95 ft. |
| Weight per Yard of Lightest Rail advisable ... ... ... | 18 lbs. |
| Load Engine will haul on Level ... ... ... ... ... | 202 tons |
| ,, ,, ,, up Incline of 1 in 100 ... ... ... ... | 98 ,, |
| ,, ,, ,, ,, ,, 1 in 50 ... ... ... ... | 56 ,, |

*Code Word—***BOWES**

## 0-6-0 TYPE

# SINGLE RAIL TENDER ENGINE

| | |
|---|---|
| Gauge of Railway ... ... ... ... ... ... ... ... | Single Rail |
| Size of Cylinders ... ... ... ... ... ... ... ... | 7 in. dia. × 12 in. stroke |
| Dia. of Coupled Wheels ... ... ... ... ... ... ... | 2 ft. 0 in. |
| ,, Tender Wheels ... ... ... ... ... ... ... | 2 ,, 0 ,, |
| Rigid Wheelbase (Engine) ... ... ... ... ... ... | 5 ,, 8 ,, |
| Total Wheelbase (Engine) ... ... ... ... ... ... | 5 ,, 8 ,, |
| ,, ,, (Engine and Tender) ... ... ... ... ... | 15 ,, 1¼ ,, |
| Height from Rail to Top of Chimney (Elevated Rail) ... ... ... | 4 ,, 5½ ,, |
| Extreme Width ... ... ... ... ... ... ... | 8 ,, 0 ,, |
| Heating Surface—Small Tubes ... ... ... 114 sq. ft. ⎫ Total for | |
| ,, ,, Firebox ... ... ... 29 ,, ⎬ Twin Boilers | |
| Total ... ... 143 ,, ... ... ... | 143 sq. ft. |
| Grate Area (Twin Fireboxes) ... ... ... ... ... ... | 5 ,, |
| Working Pressure ... ... ... ... ... ... ... | 150 lbs. per sq. in. |
| Tank Capacity ... ... ... ... ... ... ... | 200 gallons |
| Fuel Space (Coal) ... ... ... ... ... ... ... | 8 cwts. |
| Weight in Working Order (Engine) ... ... ... ... ... ... | (about) 6 tons 0 cwts. |
| ,, ,, ,, (Tender) ... ... ... ... ... | ( ,, ) 4 ,, 0 ,, |
| Total Weight of Engine and Tender in Working Order ... ... .. | ( ,, ) 10 ,, 0 ,, |
| ,, ,, on Coupled Wheels ... ... ... ... | ( ,, ) 6 ,, 0 ,, |
| Tractive Effort at 75 per cent. of Boiler Pressure ... ... ... | 2751 lbs. |
| Ratio Adhesive Weight ÷ Tractive Effort ... ... ... ... | 4·9 |
| Minimum Radius of Curve Engine will traverse with ease ... ... | 100 ft. |
| Load Engine will haul on Level ... ... ... ... ... | 140 tons |
| ,, ,, ,, up Incline of 1 in 100 ... ... ... ... | 70 ,, |
| ,, ,, ,, ,, ,, 1 in 50 ... ... ... ... | 40 ,, |

*Code Word—***LARTI**

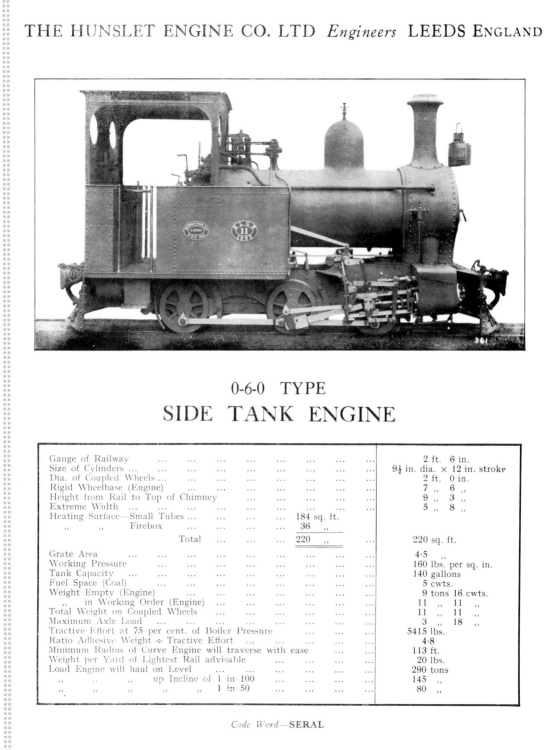

## 0-6-0 TYPE
# SIDE TANK ENGINE

| | |
|---|---|
| Gauge of Railway | 2 ft. 6 in. |
| Size of Cylinders | 9½ in. dia. × 12 in. stroke |
| Dia. of Coupled Wheels | 2 ft. 0 in. |
| Rigid Wheelbase (Engine) | 7 ,, 6 ,, |
| Height from Rail to Top of Chimney | 9 ,, 3 ,, |
| Extreme Width | 5 ,, 8 ,, |
| Heating Surface—Small Tubes ... 184 sq. ft. | |
| ,, ,, Firebox ... 36 ,, | |
| Total ... 220 ,, | 220 sq. ft. |
| Grate Area | 4·5 ,, |
| Working Pressure | 160 lbs. per sq. in. |
| Tank Capacity | 140 gallons |
| Fuel Space (Coal) | 5 cwts. |
| Weight Empty (Engine) | 9 tons 16 cwts. |
| ,, in Working Order (Engine) | 11 ,, 11 ,, |
| Total Weight on Coupled Wheels | 11 ,, 11 ,, |
| Maximum Axle Load | 3 ,, 18 ,, |
| Tractive Effort at 75 per cent. of Boiler Pressure | 5415 lbs. |
| Ratio Adhesive Weight ÷ Tractive Effort | 4·8 |
| Minimum Radius of Curve Engine will traverse with ease | 113 ft. |
| Weight per Yard of Lightest Rail advisable | 20 lbs. |
| Load Engine will haul on Level | 290 tons |
| ,, ,, ,, up Incline of 1 in 100 | 145 ,, |
| ,, ,, ,, ,, ,, 1 in 50 | 80 ,, |

*Code Word*—**SERAL**

# THE HUNSLET ENGINE CO. LTD *Engineers* LEEDS ENGLAND

## 0-4-2 TYPE
## SIDE TANK ENGINE

| | |
|---|---|
| Gauge of Railway ... ... ... ... ... ... ... ... | 2 ft. 6 in. |
| Size of Cylinders ... ... ... ... ... ... ... ... | 8½ in. dia. × 14 in. stroke |
| Dia. of Coupled Wheels ... ... ... ... ... ... ... | 2 ft. 6 in. |
| ,, Bogie Wheels ... ... ... ... ... ... ... | 1 ,, 10½ ,, |
| Rigid Wheelbase (Engine) ... ... ... ... ... ... | 4 ,, 9 ,, |
| Total Wheelbase (Engine) ... ... ... ... ... ... | 10 ,, 3 ,, |
| Height from Rail to Top of Chimney ... ... ... ... | 10 ,, 1 ,, |
| Extreme Width ... ... ... ... ... ... ... ... | 7 ,, 2 ,, |
| Heating Surface—Small Tubes ... ... ... ... 201 sq. ft. | |
| ,, ,, Firebox ... ... ... ... 35 ,, | |
| Total ... ... ... 236 ,, ... | 236 sq. ft. |
| Grate Area ... ... ... ... ... ... ... ... | 7·36 ,, |
| Working Pressure ... ... ... ... ... ... ... | 160 lbs. per sq. in. |
| Tank Capacity ... ... ... ... ... ... ... ... | 250 gallons |
| Fuel Space (Coal) ... ... ... ... ... ... ... | 15 cwts. |
| Weight Empty (Engine) ... ... ... ... ... ... | 12 tons 7 cwts. |
| Weight in Working Order (Engine) ... ... ... ... ... | 14 ,, 9 ,, |
| Total Weight on Coupled Wheels ... ... ... ... ... | 11 ,, 5 ,, |
| Maximum Axle Load ... ... ... ... ... ... ... | 5 ,, 15 ,, |
| Tractive Effort at 75 per cent. of Boiler Pressure ... ... ... ... | 4045 lbs. |
| Ratio Adhesive Weight ÷ Tractive Effort ... ... ... ... | 6·2 |
| Minimum Radius of Curve Engine will traverse with ease ... ... | 120 ft. |
| Weight per Yard of Lightest Rail advisable ... ... ... ... | 30 lbs. |
| Load Engine will haul on Level ... ... ... ... ... | 210 tons |
| ,, ,, ,, up Incline of 1 in 100 ... ... ... ... | 100 ,, |
| ,, ,, ,, ,, ,, 1 in 50 ... ... ... ... | 55 ,, |

*Code Word*—**BASAT**

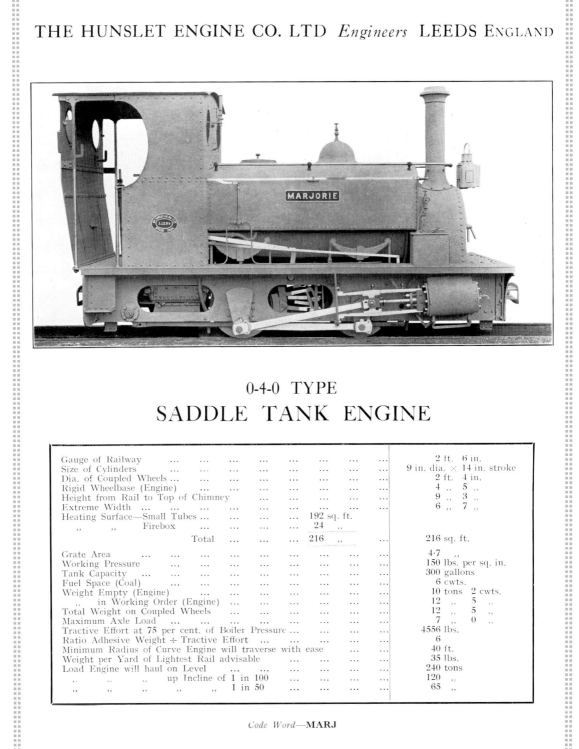

## 0-4-0 TYPE
# SADDLE TANK ENGINE

| | |
|---|---|
| Gauge of Railway | 2 ft. 6 in. |
| Size of Cylinders | 9 in. dia. × 14 in. stroke |
| Dia. of Coupled Wheels | 2 ft. 4 in. |
| Rigid Wheelbase (Engine) | 4 ,, 5 ,, |
| Height from Rail to Top of Chimney | 9 ,, 3 ,, |
| Extreme Width | 6 ,, 7 ,, |
| Heating Surface—Small Tubes | 192 sq. ft. |
| ,,    ,,    Firebox | 24 ,, |
| Total | 216 ,, ... 216 sq. ft. |
| Grate Area | 4·7 ,, |
| Working Pressure | 150 lbs. per sq. in. |
| Tank Capacity | 300 gallons |
| Fuel Space (Coal) | 6 cwts. |
| Weight Empty (Engine) | 10 tons 2 cwts. |
| ,, in Working Order (Engine) | 12 ,, 5 ,, |
| Total Weight on Coupled Wheels | 12 ,, 5 ,, |
| Maximum Axle Load | 7 ,, 0 ,, |
| Tractive Effort at 75 per cent. of Boiler Pressure | 4556 lbs. |
| Ratio Adhesive Weight ÷ Tractive Effort | 6 |
| Minimum Radius of Curve Engine will traverse with ease | 40 ft. |
| Weight per Yard of Lightest Rail advisable | 35 lbs. |
| Load Engine will haul on Level | 240 tons |
| ,, ,, ,, up Incline of 1 in 100 | 120 ,, |
| ,, ,, ,, ,, ,, 1 in 50 | 65 ,, |

*Code Word—***MARJ**

## 0-6-2 TYPE

# SIDE TANK ENGINE

| | |
|---|---|
| Gauge of Railway ... ... ... ... ... ... ... ... | 1 ft. 11⅝ in. |
| Size of Cylinders ... ... ... ... ... ... ... ... ... | 10¾ in. dia. × 15 in. stroke |
| Dia. of Coupled Wheels ... ... ... ... ... ... ... | 2 ft. 4 in. |
| ,, Bogie Wheels ... ... ... ... ... ... ... | 1 ,, 6 ,, |
| Rigid Wheelbase (Engine) ... ... ... ... ... ... | 5 ,, 6 ,, |
| Total Wheelbase (Engine) ... ... ... ... ... ... | 11 ,, 4 ,, |
| Height from Rail to Top of Chimney ... ... ... ... | 9 ,, 6 ,, |
| Extreme Width ... ... ... ... ... ... ... ... | 6 ,, 8 ,, |
| Heating Surface—Small Tubes ... ... ... 345 sq. ft. | |
| ,, ,, Firebox ... ... ... ... 36 ,, | |
| Total ... ... ... 381 ,, ... | 381 sq. ft. |
| Grate Area ... ... ... ... ... ... ... ... ... | 6·25 ,, |
| Working Pressure ... ... ... ... ... ... ... ... | 160 lbs. per sq. in. |
| Tank Capacity ... ... ... ... ... ... ... ... | 340 gallons |
| Fuel Space (Coal) ... ... ... ... ... ... ... ... | 13 cwts. |
| Weight Empty (Engine) ... ... ... ... ... ... ... | 14 tons 0 cwts. |
| ,, in Working Order (Engine) ... ... ... ... | 18 ,, 10 ,, |
| Total Weight on Coupled Wheels ... ... ... ... ... | 14 ,, 15 ,, |
| Maximum Axle Load ... ... ... ... ... ... ... | 5 ,, 0 ,, |
| Tractive Effort at 75 per cent. of Boiler Pressure ... ... ... | 7425 lbs. |
| Ratio Adhesive Weight ÷ Tractive Effort ... ... ... ... | 4·4 |
| Minimum Radius of Curve Engine will traverse with ease ... ... | 80 ft. |
| Weight per Yard of Lightest Rail advisable ... ... ... | 30 lbs. |
| Load Engine will haul on Level ... ... ... ... ... | 390 tons |
| ,, ,, ,, up Incline of 1 in 100 ... ... ... ... | 195 ,, |
| ,, ,, ,, ,, ,, 1 in 50 ... ... ... ... | 110 ,, |

*Code Word*—**MASHA**

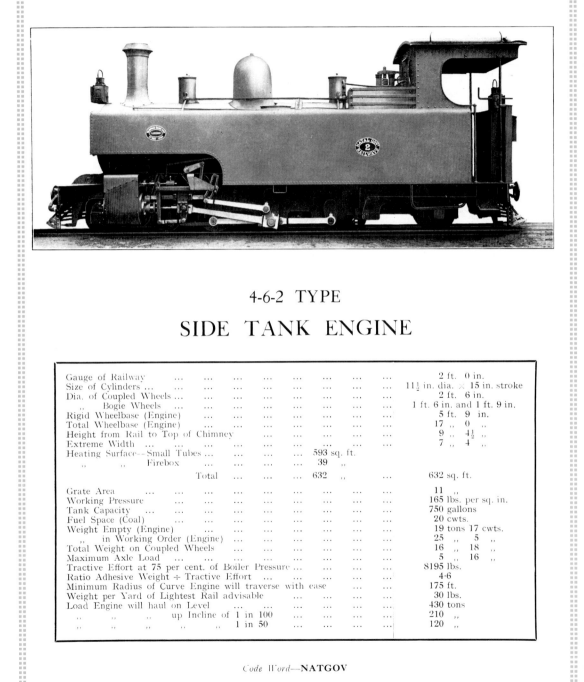

## 4-6-2 TYPE

# SIDE TANK ENGINE

| | |
|---|---|
| Gauge of Railway ... ... ... ... ... ... ... ... | 2 ft. 0 in. |
| Size of Cylinders ... ... ... ... ... ... ... ... | 11½ in. dia. × 15 in. stroke |
| Dia. of Coupled Wheels ... ... ... ... ... ... ... | 2 ft. 6 in. |
| ,, Bogie Wheels ... ... ... ... ... ... ... | 1 ft. 6 in. and 1 ft. 9 in. |
| Rigid Wheelbase (Engine) ... ... ... ... ... ... | 5 ft. 9 in. |
| Total Wheelbase (Engine) ... ... ... ... ... ... | 17 ,, 0 ,, |
| Height from Rail to Top of Chimney ... ... ... ... | 9 ,, 4½ ,, |
| Extreme Width ... ... ... ... ... ... ... ... | 7 ,, 4 ,, |
| Heating Surface—Small Tubes ... ... ... ... 593 sq. ft. | |
| ,, ,, Firebox ... ... ... ... 39 ,, | |
| Total ... ... ... 632 ,, ... ... | 632 sq. ft. |
| Grate Area ... ... ... ... ... ... ... ... | 11 ,, |
| Working Pressure ... ... ... ... ... ... ... | 165 lbs. per sq. in. |
| Tank Capacity ... ... ... ... ... ... ... ... | 750 gallons |
| Fuel Space (Coal) ... ... ... ... ... ... ... | 20 cwts. |
| Weight Empty (Engine) ... ... ... ... ... ... | 19 tons 17 cwts. |
| ,, in Working Order (Engine) ... ... ... ... | 25 ,, 5 ,, |
| Total Weight on Coupled Wheels ... ... ... ... ... | 16 ,, 18 ,, |
| Maximum Axle Load ... ... ... ... ... ... ... | 5 ,, 16 ,, |
| Tractive Effort at 75 per cent. of Boiler Pressure ... ... ... | 8195 lbs. |
| Ratio Adhesive Weight ÷ Tractive Effort ... ... ... ... | 4·6 |
| Minimum Radius of Curve Engine will traverse with ease ... ... | 175 ft. |
| Weight per Yard of Lightest Rail advisable ... ... ... | 30 lbs. |
| Load Engine will haul on Level ... ... ... ... ... | 430 tons |
| ,, ,, ,, up Incline of 1 in 100 ... ... ... ... | 210 ,, |
| ,, ,, ,, ,, ,, 1 in 50 ... ... ... ... | 120 ,, |

*Code Word—***NATGOV**

# 0-4-2 TYPE

# SIDE TANK ENGINE

| | |
|---|---|
| Gauge of Railway | 2 ft. 0 in. |
| Size of Cylinders | $8\frac{1}{2}$ in. dia. × 14 in. stroke |
| Dia. of Coupled Wheels | 2 ft. 6 in. |
| ,, Bogie Wheels | 1 ,, 9 ,, |
| Rigid Wheelbase (Engine) | 4 ,, 6 ,, |
| Total Wheelbase (Engine) | 10 ,, 6 ,, |
| Height from Rail to Top of Chimney | 8 ,, 6 ,, |
| Extreme Width | 5 ,, $6\frac{3}{4}$ ,, |
| Heating Surface—Small Tubes ... 196 sq. ft. | |
| ,, ,, Firebox ... 33 ,, | |
| Total ... 229 ,, | 229 sq. ft. |
| Grate Area | 7·36 ,, |
| Working Pressure | 160 lbs. per sq. in. |
| Tank Capacity | 250 gallons |
| Fuel Space (Coal) | 19 cwts. |
| Weight Empty (Engine) | 11 tons 0 cwts. |
| ,, in Working Order (Engine) | 15 ,, 0 ,, |
| Total Weight on Coupled Wheels | 10 ,, 15 ,, |
| Maximum Axle Load | 5 ,, 8 ,, |
| Tractive Effort at 75 per cent. of Boiler Pressure | 4045 lbs. |
| Ratio Adhesive Weight ÷ Tractive Effort | 5·9 |
| Minimum Radius of Curve Engine will traverse with ease | 130 ft. |
| Weight per Yard of Lightest Rail advisable | 30 lbs. |
| Load Engine will haul on Level | 210 tons |
| ,, ,, ,, up Incline of 1 in 100 | 100 ,, |
| ,, ,, ,, ,, ,, 1 in 50 | 55 ,, |

*Code Word*—**EVA**

## 2-6-2 TYPE

# SIDE TANK ENGINE

| | |
|---|---|
| Gauge of Railway ... ... ... ... ... ... ... ... | 2 ft. 6 in. |
| Size of Cylinders ... ... ... ... ... ... ... ... | 12¾ in. dia. × 16 in. stroke |
| Dia. of Coupled Wheels ... ... ... ... ... ... ... | 2 ft. 6 in. |
| ,,     Bogie Wheels  ... ... ... ... ... ... ... | 2 ,, 0½ ,, |
| Rigid Wheelbase (Engine) ... ... ... ... ... ... | 6 ,, 6 ,, |
| Total Wheelbase (Engine) ... ... ... ... ... ... | 18 ,, 0 ,, |
| Height from Rail to Top of Chimney ... ... ... ... | 9 ,, 9 ,, |
| Extreme Width ... ... ... ... ... ... ... ... | 8 ,, 2⅝ ,, |
| Heating Surface—Small Tubes ... ... ... ... 506 sq. ft. | |
| ,,        ,,       Firebox  ... ... ... ... 49  ,, | |
| Total  ... ... ... 555  ,, ... | 555 sq. ft. |
| Grate Area ... ... ... ... ... ... ... ... | 9  ,, |
| Working Pressure ... ... ... ... ... ... ... | 160 lbs. per sq. in. |
| Tank Capacity ... ... ... ... ... ... ... ... | 620 gallons |
| Fuel Space (Coal) ... ... ... ... ... ... ... | 2 tons 0 cwts. |
| Weight Empty (Engine) ... ... ... ... ... ... | 20 ,, 9 ,, |
| ,, in Working Order (Engine) ... ... ... ... | 25 ,, 19 ,, |
| Total Weight on Coupled Wheels ... ... ... ... | 19 ,, 15 ,, |
| Maximum Axle Load  ... ... ... ... ... ... | 7 ,, 0 ,, |
| Tractive Effort at 75 per cent. of Boiler Pressure ... | 10400 lbs. |
| Ratio Adhesive Weight ÷ Tractive Effort ... ... ... | 4·3 |
| Minimum Radius of Curve Engine will traverse with ease ... | 150 ft. |
| Weight per Yard of Lightest Rail advisable ... ... ... | 35 lbs. |
| Load Engine will haul on Level ... ... ... ... | 555 tons |
| ,,    ,,    ,,    up Incline of 1 in 100 ... ... ... | 275 ,, |
| ,,    ,,    ,,    ,,    ,,  1 in 50 ... ... ... | 155 ,, |

*Code Word—*JUMNA

# THE HUNSLET ENGINE CO. LTD *Engineers* LEEDS ENGLAND

## 2-8-0 TYPE

# TENDER ENGINE

| | |
|---|---|
| Gauge of Railway ... ... ... ... ... ... ... ... | 2 ft. 6 in. |
| Size of Cylinders ... ... ... ... ... ... ... ... | 16½ in. dia. × 20 in. stroke |
| Dia. of Coupled Wheels ... ... ... ... ... ... ... | 3 ft. 1½ in. |
| ,,    Bogie Wheels ... ... ... ... ... ... ... | 2 ,, 3 ,, |
| ,,    Tender Wheels ... ... ... ... ... ... ... | 2 ,, 3 ,, |
| Rigid Wheelbase (Engine) ... ... ... ... ... ... | 10 ,, 7 ,, |
| Total Wheelbase (Engine) ... ... ... ... ... ... | 17 ,, 1 ,, |
| ,,    ,,    (Engine and Tender) ... ... ... ... | 44 ,, 4 ,, |
| Height from Rail to Top of Chimney ... ... ... ... | 11 ,, 6 ,, |
| Heating Surface—Small Tubes ... ... ... 1148 sq. ft. | |
| ,,    ,,    Firebox ... ... ... 88 ,, | |
| Total ... ... ... 1236 ,, ... | 1236 sq. ft. |
| Grate Area ... ... ... ... ... ... ... ... ... | 20 ,, |
| Working Pressure ... ... ... ... ... ... ... ... | 180 lbs. per sq. in. |
| Tank Capacity ... ... ... ... ... ... ... ... | 2500 gallons |
| Fuel Space (Coal) ... ... ... ... ... ... ... ... | 6 tons 5 cwts. |
| Weight Empty (Engine) ... ... ... ... ... ... ... | 39 ,, 19 ,, |
| ,,    ,,    (Tender) ... ... ... ... ... ... | 12 ,, 11 ,, |
| ,,    in Working Order (Engine) ... ... ... ... ... | 44 ,, 5 ,, |
| ,,    ,,    ,,    (Tender) ... ... ... ... ... | 29 ,, 17 ,, |
| Total Weight of Engine and Tender in Working Order ... | 74 ,, 2 ,, |
| ,,    ,,    on Coupled Wheels ... ... ... ... | 40 ,, 7 ,, |
| Maximum Axle Load ... ... ... ... ... ... ... | 11 ,, 9 ,, |
| Tractive Effort at 75 per cent. of Boiler Pressure ... ... | 19600 lbs. |
| Ratio Adhesive Weight ÷ Tractive Effort ... ... ... ... | 4·6 |
| Minimum Radius of Curve Engine will traverse with ease ... | 240 ft. |
| Weight per Yard of Lightest Rail advisable ... ... ... | 60 lbs. |
| Load Engine will haul on Level ... ... ... ... ... | 1015 tons |
| ,,    ,,    ,,    up Incline of 1 in 100 ... ... ... | 495 ,, |
| ,,    ,,    ,,    ,,    ,,    1 in 50 ... ... ... | 270 ,, |

*Code Word—***DIANA**

## 0-6-0 TYPE

# SADDLE TANK ENGINE

| | |
|---|---|
| Gauge of Railway ... ... ... ... ... ... ... ... ... | 3 ft. 3¾ in. |
| Size of Cylinders ... ... ... ... ... ... ... ... ... | 10 in. dia. × 16 in. stroke |
| Dia. of Coupled Wheels ... ... ... ... ... ... ... ... | 2 ft. 9 in. |
| Total Wheelbase (Engine) ... ... ... ... ... ... ... | 8 ,, 9 ,, |
| Height from Rail to Top of Chimney ... ... ... ... | 10 ,, 0 ,, |
| Extreme Width ... ... ... ... ... ... ... ... ... | 6 ,, 5 ,, |
| Heating Surface—Small Tubes ... ... ... ... 305 sq. ft. | |
| ,, ,, Firebox ... ... ... ... 35 ,, | |
| Total ... ... ... 340 ,, ... | 340 sq. ft. |
| Grate Area ... ... ... ... ... ... ... ... ... | 5·2 ,, |
| Working Pressure ... ... ... ... ... ... ... ... | 160 lbs. per sq. in. |
| Tank Capacity ... ... ... ... ... ... ... ... ... | 350 gallons |
| Fuel Space (Coal) ... ... ... ... ... ... ... ... | 12 cwts. |
| Weight Empty (Engine) ... ... ... ... ... ... ... | 15 tons 7 cwts. |
| ,, in Working Order (Engine) ... ... ... ... | 18 ,, 14 ,, |
| Total Weight on Coupled Wheels ... ... ... ... ... | 18 ,, 14 ,, |
| Maximum Axle Load ... ... ... ... ... ... ... | 6 ,, 18 ,, |
| Tractive Effort at 75 per cent. of Boiler Pressure ... ... ... ... | 5818 lbs. |
| Ratio Adhesive Weight ÷ Tractive Effort ... ... ... ... | 7·2 |
| Minimum Radius of Curve Engine will traverse with ease ... ... | 155 ft. |
| Weight per Yard of Lightest Rail advisable ... ... ... ... | 35 lbs. |
| Load Engine will haul on Level ... ... ... ... ... ... | 305 tons |
| ,, ,, ,, up Incline of 1 in 100 ... ... ... | 150 ,, |
| ,, ,, ,, ,, 1 in 50 ... ... ... | 85 ,, |

*Code Word*—**CENCHU**

## 0-6-0 TYPE
# SADDLE TANK ENGINE

| | |
|---|---|
| Gauge of Railway ... ... ... ... ... ... ... ... | 2 ft. 0 in. |
| Size of Cylinders ... ... ... ... ... ... ... ... | 8 in. dia. × 10 in. stroke |
| Dia. of Coupled Wheels ... ... ... ... ... ... ... | 1 ft. 8 in. |
| Total Wheelbase ... ... ... ... ... ... ... ... | 5 ,, 0 ,, |
| Height from Rail to Top of Chimney ... ... ... ... | 8 ,, 2 ,, |
| Extreme Width ... ... ... ... ... ... ... ... | 6 ,, 4 ,, |
| Heating Surface—Small Tubes ... ... ... ... 117 sq. ft. | |
| ,, ,, Firebox ... ... ... 21 ,, | |
| Total ... ... ... 138 ,, ... | 138 sq. ft. |
| Grate Area ... ... ... ... ... ... ... ... | 4 ,, |
| Working Pressure ... ... ... ... ... ... ... | 160 lbs. per sq. in. |
| Tank Capacity ... ... ... ... ... ... ... ... | 220 gallons |
| Fuel Space (Coal) ... ... ... ... ... ... ... | 3 cwts. |
| Weight Empty ... ... ... ... ... ... ... ... | 8 tons 2 cwts. |
| ,, in Working Order ... ... ... ... ... ... | 9 ,, 17 ,, |
| Total Weight on Coupled Wheels ... ... ... ... | 9 ,, 17 ,, |
| Maximum Axle Load ... ... ... ... ... ... ... | 4 ,, 17 ,, |
| Tractive Effort at 75 per cent. of Boiler Pressure ... ... ... | 3840 lbs. |
| Ratio Adhesive Weight ÷ Tractive Effort ... ... ... ... | 5·8 |
| Minimum Radius of Curve Engine will traverse with ease ... ... | 50 ft. |
| Weight per Yard of Lightest Rail advisable ... ... ... | 25 lbs. |
| Load Engine will haul on Level ... ... ... ... ... | 200 tons |
| ,, ,, ,, up Incline of 1 in 100 ... ... ... | 100 ,, |
| ,, ,, ,, ,, ,, 1 in 50 ... ... ... | 55 ,, |

*Code Word*—**GROBI**

# THE HUNSLET ENGINE CO. LTD *Engineers* LEEDS ENGLAND

## 0-4-0 TYPE

# SIDE TANK ENGINE

| | |
|---|---|
| Gauge of Railway ... ... ... ... ... ... ... ... | 2 ft. 6 in. |
| Size of Cylinders ... ... ... ... ... ... ... ... | 5 in. dia. × 8 in. stroke |
| Dia. of Coupled Wheels ... ... ... ... ... ... ... | 1 ft. 6 in. |
| Rigid Wheelbase (Engine) ... ... ... ... ... ... | 3 ,, 0 ,, |
| Height from Rail to Top of Chimney ... ... ... ... | 7 ,, 2¼ ,, |
| Extreme Width ... ... ... ... ... ... ... ... | 4 ,, 9 ,, |
| Heating Surface—Small Tubes ... ... ... ... 45 sq. ft. | |
| ,, ,, Firebox ... ... ... 10 ,, | |
| Total ... ... ... 55 ,, ... | 55 sq. ft. |
| Grate Area ... ... ... ... ... ... ... ... | 2 ,, |
| Working Pressure ... ... ... ... ... ... ... | 160 lbs. per sq. in. |
| Tank Capacity ... ... ... ... ... ... ... ... | 65 gallons |
| Fuel Space (Coal) ... ... ... ... ... ... ... | 3 cwts. |
| Weight Empty (Engine) ... ... ... ... ... ... | 4 tons 0 cwts. |
| ,, in Working Order (Engine) ... ... ... ... | 4 ,, 14 ,, |
| Total Weight on Coupled Wheels ... ... ... ... ... | 4 ,, 14 ,, |
| Maximum Axle Load ... ... ... ... ... ... ... | 2 ,, 16 ,, |
| Tractive Effort at 75 per cent. of Boiler Pressure ... ... ... | 1333 lbs. |
| Ratio Adhesive Weight ÷ Tractive Effort ... ... ... | 7·8 |
| Minimum Radius of Curve Engine will traverse with ease ... ... | 20 ft. |
| Weight per Yard of Lightest Rail advisable ... ... ... | 15 lbs. |
| Load Engine will haul on Level ... ... ... ... ... | 70 tons |
| ,, ,, ,, up Incline of 1 in 100 ... ... ... | 33 ,, |
| ,, ,, ,, ,, ,, 1 in 50 ... ... ... | 18 ,, |

*Code Word* —**BENG**

## 0-4-0 TYPE

# SIDE TANK ENGINE

| | |
|---|---|
| Gauge of Railway ... ... ... ... ... ... ... | 1 ft. 11⅝ in. |
| Size of Cylinders ... ... ... ... ... ... ... ... | 7 in. dia. × 12 in. stroke |
| Dia. of Coupled Wheels ... ... ... ... ... ... | 2 ft. 0 in. |
| Rigid Wheelbase (Engine) ... ... ... ... ... | 4 ,, 0 ,, |
| Height from Rail to Top of Chimney ... ... ... | 8 ,, 2¼ ,, |
| Extreme Width ... ... ... ... ... ... ... | 5 ,, 7½ ,, |
| Heating Surface—Small Tubes ... ... ... ... 111 sq. ft. | |
| ,, ,, Firebox ... ... ... ... 15 ,, | |
| Total ... ... ... 126 ,, ... | 126 sq. ft. |
| Grate Area ... ... ... ... ... ... ... ... | 3 ,, |
| Working Pressure ... ... ... ... ... ... | 160 lbs. per sq. in. |
| Tank Capacity ... ... ... ... ... ... ... | 180 gallons |
| Fuel Space (Coal) ... ... ... ... ... ... ... | 3 cwts. |
| Weight Empty (Engine) ... ... ... ... ... ... | 7 tons 4 cwts. |
| ,, in Working Order (Engine) ... ... ... | 8 ,, 14 ,, |
| Total Weight on Coupled Wheels ... ... ... ... | 8 ,, 14 ,, |
| Maximum Axle Load ... ... ... ... ... ... | 5 ,, 5 ,, |
| Tractive Effort at 75 per cent. of Boiler Pressure ... ... ... | 2940 lbs. |
| Ratio Adhesive Weight ÷ Tractive Effort ... ... ... ... | 6·6 |
| Minimum Radius of Curve Engine will traverse with ease ... ... | 32 ft. |
| Weight per Yard of Lightest Rail advisable ... ... ... ... | 30 lbs. |
| Load Engine will haul on Level ... ... ... ... ... | 150 tons |
| ,, ,, ,, up Incline of 1 in 100 ... ... ... | 75 ,, |
| ,, ,, ,, ,, ,, 1 in 50 ... ... ... ... | 40 ,, |

*Code Word*—**MICRO**

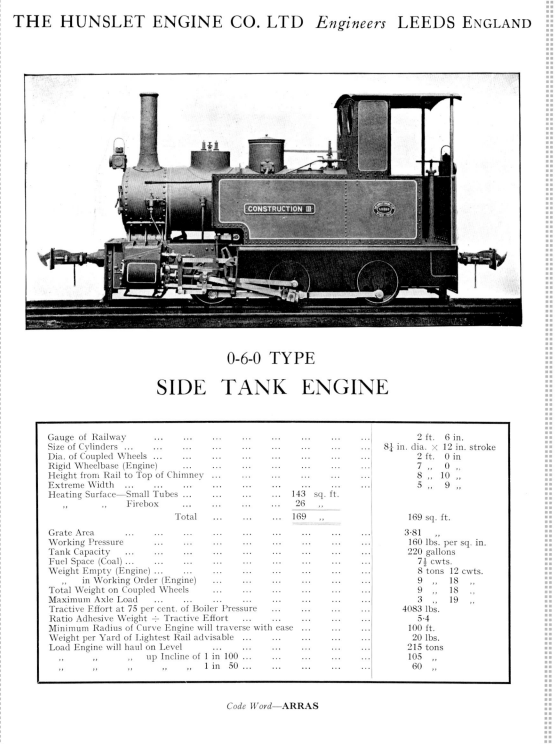

## 0-6-0 TYPE

# SIDE TANK ENGINE

| | |
|---|---|
| Gauge of Railway ... ... ... ... ... ... ... ... | 2 ft. 6 in. |
| Size of Cylinders ... ... ... ... ... ... ... ... | 8¼ in. dia. × 12 in. stroke |
| Dia. of Coupled Wheels ... ... ... ... ... ... ... | 2 ft. 0 in |
| Rigid Wheelbase (Engine) ... ... ... ... ... ... ... | 7 ,, 0 ,, |
| Height from Rail to Top of Chimney ... ... ... ... ... | 8 ,, 10 ,, |
| Extreme Width ... ... ... ... ... ... ... ... | 5 ,, 9 ,, |
| Heating Surface—Small Tubes ... ... ... ... 143 sq. ft. | |
| ,, ,, Firebox ... ... ... ... 26 ,, | |
| Total ... ... ... 169 ,, | 169 sq. ft. |
| Grate Area ... ... ... ... ... ... ... ... | 3·81 ,, |
| Working Pressure ... ... ... ... ... ... ... | 160 lbs. per sq. in. |
| Tank Capacity ... ... ... ... ... ... ... | 220 gallons |
| Fuel Space (Coal) ... ... ... ... ... ... ... | 7½ cwts. |
| Weight Empty (Engine) ... ... ... ... ... ... | 8 tons 12 cwts. |
| ,, in Working Order (Engine) ... ... ... ... | 9 ,, 18 ,, |
| Total Weight on Coupled Wheels ... ... ... ... ... | 9 ,, 18 ,, |
| Maximum Axle Load ... ... ... ... ... ... | 3 ,, 19 ,, |
| Tractive Effort at 75 per cent. of Boiler Pressure ... ... ... | 4083 lbs. |
| Ratio Adhesive Weight ÷ Tractive Effort ... ... ... | 5·4 |
| Minimum Radius of Curve Engine will traverse with ease ... ... | 100 ft. |
| Weight per Yard of Lightest Rail advisable ... ... ... ... | 20 lbs. |
| Load Engine will haul on Level ... ... ... ... ... | 215 tons |
| ,, ,, ,, up Incline of 1 in 100 ... ... ... ... | 105 ,, |
| ,, ,, ,, ,, ,, 1 in 50 ... ... ... ... | 60 ,, |

*Code Word—*ARRAS

# THE HUNSLET ENGINE CO. LTD *Engineers* LEEDS ENGLAND

## 0-4-0 TYPE

# SIDE TANK ENGINE

| | |
|---|---|
| Gauge of Railway ... ... ... ... ... ... ... ... | 2 ft. 6 in. |
| Size of Cylinders ... ... ... ... ... ... ... ... | 7 in. dia. × 12 in. stroke |
| Dia. of Coupled Wheels ... ... ... ... ... ... ... | 2 ft. 0 in. |
| Rigid Wheelbase (Engine) ... ... ... ... ... ... | 4 0 ,, |
| Height from Rail to Top of Chimney ... ... ... ... | 8 ,, 9 ,, |
| Extreme Width ... ... ... ... ... ... ... ... | 6 ,, 5¼ ,, |
| Heating Surface—Small Tubes ... ... ... 112 sq. ft. | |
| ,, ,, Firebox ... ... ... 27 ,, | |
| Total ... ... ... 139 ,, ... | 139 sq. ft. |
| Grate Area ... ... ... ... ... ... ... ... | 4 ,, |
| Working Pressure ... ... ... ... ... ... ... | 160 lbs. per sq. in. |
| Tank Capacity ... ... ... ... ... ... ... | 250 gallons |
| Fuel Space (Oil) ... ... ... ... ... ... ... | 50 ,, |
| Weight Empty (Engine) ... ... ... ... ... ... | 7 tons 15 cwts. |
| ,, in Working Order (Engine) ... ... ... ... | 9 ,, 15 ,, |
| Total Weight on Coupled Wheels ... ... ... ... | 9 ,, 15 ,, |
| Tractive Effort at 75 per cent. of Boiler Pressure ... ... ... | 2940 lbs. |
| Ratio Adhesive Weight ÷ Tractive Effort ... ... ... ... | 7·4 |
| Minimum Radius of Curve Engine will traverse with ease ... ... | 30 ft. |
| Weight per Yard of Lightest Rail advisable ... ... ... | 25 lbs. |
| Load Engine will haul on Level ... ... ... ... ... | 155 tons |
| ,, ,, ,, up Incline of 1 in 100 ... ... ... | 75 ,, |
| ,, ,, ,, ,, ,, 1 in 50 ... ... ... | 40 ,, |

*Code Word*—**FORTU**

## 0-4-0 TYPE

# SADDLE TANK ENGINE

| | |
|---|---|
| Gauge of Railway ... ... ... ... ... ... ... ... | 3 ft. 0 in. |
| Size of Cylinders ... ... ... ... ... ... ... ... | 7 in. dia. × 10 in. stroke |
| Dia. of Coupled Wheels ... ... ... ... ... ... ... | 1 ft. 8 in. |
| Rigid Wheelbase (Engine) ... ... ... ... ... ... | 3 ,, 3 ,, |
| Height from Rail to Top of Chimney ... ... ... | 9 ,, 6 ,, |
| Extreme Width ... ... ... ... ... ... ... ... | 6 ,, 5$\frac{3}{8}$ ,, |
| Heating Surface—Small Tubes ... ... ... ... 101 sq. ft. | |
| ,, ,, Firebox ... ... ... ... 18 ,, | |
| Total ... ... ... 119 ,, ... | 119 sq. ft. |
| Grate Area ... ... ... ... ... ... ... ... | 2·8 ,, |
| Working Pressure ... ... ... ... ... ... ... | 160 lbs. per sq. in. |
| Tank Capacity ... ... ... ... ... ... ... ... | 120 gallons |
| Fuel Space (Coal) ... ... ... ... ... ... ... | 3$\frac{1}{2}$ cwts. |
| Weight Empty (Engine) ... ... ... ... ... ... | 7 tons 16 cwts. |
| ,, in Working Order (Engine) ... ... ... ... | 8 ,, 19 ,, |
| Total Weight on Coupled Wheels ... ... ... ... | 8 ,, 19 ,, |
| Maximum Axle Load ... ... ... ... ... ... ... | 4 ,, 11 ,, |
| Tractive Effort at 75 per cent. of Boiler Pressure ... ... ... | 2940 lbs. |
| Ratio Adhesive Weight ÷ Tractive Effort ... ... ... ... | 6·7 |
| Minimum Radius of Curve Engine will traverse with ease ... ... | 20 ft. |
| Weight per Yard of Lightest Rail advisable ... ... ... ... | 25 lbs. |
| Load Engine will haul on Level ... ... ... ... ... | 150 tons |
| ,, ,, ,, up Incline of 1 in 100 ... ... ... ... | 75 ,, |
| ,, ,, ,, ,, ,, 1 in 50 ... ... ... ... | 40 ,, |

*Code Word—***KYSTIM**

# THE HUNSLET ENGINE CO. LTD *Engineers* LEEDS ENGLAND

## 0-6-0 TYPE

# TENDER ENGINE

| | |
|---|---|
| Gauge of Railway ... ... ... ... ... ... ... ... | 2 ft. 6 in. |
| Size of Cylinders ... ... ... ... ... ... ... ... | 8 in. dia. × 12 in. stroke |
| Dia. of Coupled Wheels ... ... ... ... ... ... ... | 2 ft. 6 in. |
| ,, Tender Wheels ... ... ... ... ... ... ... | 2 ,, 0 ,, |
| Rigid Wheelbase (Engine) ... ... ... ... ... ... | 7 ,, 4 ,, |
| Total Wheelbase (Engine) ... ... ... ... ... ... | 7 ,, 4 ,, |
| ,, ,, (Engine and Tender) ... ... ... ... | 17 ,, 7 ,, |
| Height from Rail to Top of Chimney ... ... ... ... | 9 ,, 4¾ ,, |
| Extreme Width ... ... ... ... ... ... ... ... | 5 ,, 2¾ ,, |
| Heating Surface—Small Tubes ... ... ... ... 127 sq. ft. ... | |
| ,, ,, Firebox ... ... ... ... 26 ,, ... | |
| Total ... ... 153 ,, ... | 153 sq. ft. |
| Grate Area ... ... ... ... ... ... ... ... | 3·75 |
| Working Pressure ... ... ... ... ... ... ... | 160 lbs. per sq. in. |
| Tank Capacity ... ... ... ... ... ... ... ... | 350 gallons |
| Fuel Space (Wood) ... ... ... ... ... ... ... | 1 ton 0 cwt. |
| Weight Empty (Engine) ... ... ... ... ... ... | 8 tons 1 ,, |
| ,, ,, (Tender) ... ... ... ... ... ... | 2 ,, 15 cwts. |
| ,, in Working Order (Engine) ... ... ... ... | 8 ,, 16 ,, |
| ,, ,, ,, (Tender) ... ... ... ... | 4 ,, 15 ,, |
| Total Weight of Engine and Tender in Working Order ... | 13 ,, 11 ,, |
| ,, ,, on Coupled Wheels ... ... ... ... | 8 ,, 16 ,, |
| Maximum Axle Load ... ... ... ... ... ... ... | 3 ,, 9 ,, |
| Tractive Effort at 75 per cent. of Boiler Pressure ... ... ... | 3072 lbs. |
| Ratio Adhesive Weight ÷ Tractive Effort ... ... ... ... | 6·4 |
| Minimum Radius of Curve Engine will traverse with ease ... ... | 110 ft. |
| Weight per Yard of Lightest Rail advisable ... ... ... ... | 20 lbs. |
| Load Engine will haul on Level ... ... ... ... ... | 155 tons |
| ,, ,, ,, up Incline of 1 in 100 ... ... ... | 75 ,, |
| ,, ,, ,, ,, ,, 1 in 50 ... ... ... ... | 40 ,, |

*Code Word*—**JOHOR**

## 0-6-4  TYPE

# SIDE  TANK  ENGINE

| | |
|---|---|
| Gauge of Railway ... ... ... ... ... ... ... ... | 2 ft.  0 in. |
| Size of Cylinders ... ... ... ... ... ... ... ... | 13 in. dia. × 18 in. stroke |
| Dia. of Coupled Wheels ... ... ... ... ... ... ... | 2 ft.  6 in. |
| ,,   Bogie Wheels ... ... ... ... ... ... ... | 1 ,,  6 ,, |
| Rigid Wheelbase (Engine) ... ... ... ... ... ... | 5 ,, 10 ,, |
| Total Wheelbase (Engine) ... ... ... ... ... ... | 15 ,,  9 ,, |
| Height from Rail to Top of Chimney ... ... ... ... | 10 ,,  0 ,, |
| Extreme Width ... ... ... ... ... ... ... ... | 7 ,,  1½ ,, |
| Heating Surface—Small Tubes ... ... ... 440 sq. ft. | |
| ,,   ,,   Firebox ... ... ... 48 ,, | |
| Total ... ... ... 488 ,, | 488 sq. ft. |
| Grate Area ... ... ... ... ... ... ... ... | 9 ,, |
| Working Pressure ... ... ... ... ... ... ... | 160 lbs. per sq. in. |
| Tank Capacity ... ... ... ... ... ... ... ... | 700 gallons |
| Fuel Space (Coal) ... ... ... ... ... ... ... | 1 ton  7 cwts. |
| Weight Empty (Engine) ... ... ... ... ... ... | 20 tons 12 ,, |
| ,,   in Working Order (Engine) ... ... ... | 26 ,,  7 ,, |
| Total Weight on Coupled Wheels ... ... ... ... | 18 ,, 17 ,, |
| Maximum Axle Load ... ... ... ... ... ... | 6 ,,  6 ,, |
| Tractive Effort at 75 per cent. of Boiler Pressure ... ... ... | 12168 lbs. |
| Ratio Adhesive Weight ÷ Tractive Effort ... ... ... ... | 3·47 |
| Minimum Radius of Curve Engine will traverse with ease ... ... | 155 ft. |
| Weight per Yard of Lightest Rail advisable ... ... ... | 35 lbs. |
| Load Engine will haul on Level ... ... ... ... ... | 650 tons |
| ,,   ,,   ,,   up Incline of 1 in 100 ... ... ... | 325 ,, |
| ,,   ,,   ,,   ,,   ,,   1 in 50 ... ... ... | 185 ,, |

*Code Word—***BOLIV**

## 0-6-0 TYPE
# SIDE TANK ENGINE

| | |
|---|---|
| Gauge of Railway | 3 ft. 0 in. |
| Size of Cylinders | 11½ in. dia. × 16 in. stroke |
| Dia. of Coupled Wheels | 2 ft. 6 in. |
| Total Wheelbase (Engine) | 10 ,, 0 ,, |
| Height from Rail to Top of Chimney | 10 ,, 3 ,, |
| Extreme Width | 7 ,, 4 ,, |
| Heating Surface—Small Tubes | 331 sq. ft. |
| ,,          ,,          Firebox | 54 ,, |
| Total | 385 ,, 385 sq. ft. |
| Grate Area | 7 ,, |
| Working Pressure | 160 lbs. per sq. in. |
| Tank Capacity | 580 gallons |
| Fuel Space (Coal) | 17 cwts. |
| Weight Empty (Engine) | 16 tons 11 cwts. |
| ,,    in Working Order (Engine) | 20 ,, 19 ,, |
| Total Weight on Coupled Wheels | 20 ,, 19 ,, |
| Maximum Axle Load | 7 ,, 1 ,, |
| Tractive Effort at 75 per cent. of Boiler Pressure | 8464 lbs. |
| Ratio Adhesive Weight ÷ Tractive Effort | 5·5 |
| Minimum Radius of Curve Engine will traverse with ease | 260 ft. |
| Weight per Yard of Lightest Rail advisable | 40 lbs. |
| Load Engine will haul on Level | 450 tons |
| ,,      ,,      ,,    up Incline of 1 in 100 | 225 ,, |
| ,,      ,,      ,,      ,,    ,,    1 in 50 | 125 ,, |

*Code Word*—**BRIHO**

## 2-6-0 TYPE

# TENDER ENGINE

| | |
|---|---|
| Gauge of Railway ... ... ... ... ... ... ... ... | 3 ft. 0 in. |
| Size of Cylinders ... ... ... ... ... ... ... ... | 15 in. dia. × 20 in. stroke |
| Dia. of Coupled Wheels ... ... ... ... ... ... ... | 3 ft. 4½ in. |
| ,, Bogie Wheels ... ... ... ... ... ... ... | 2 ,, 3½ ,, |
| Rigid Wheelbase (Engine) ... ... ... ... ... ... | 8 ,, 9 ,, |
| Total Wheelbase (Engine) ... ... ... ... ... ... | 16 ,, 9 ,, |
| ,, ,, (Engine and Tender) ... ... ... | 38 ,, 11 ,, |
| Height from Rail to Top of Chimney ... ... ... ... ... | 11 ,, 3 ,, |
| Extreme Width ... ... ... ... ... ... ... ... | 8 ,, 6 ,, |
| Heating Surface—Small Tubes ... ... ... ... 703·5 sq. ft. | |
| ,, ,, Firebox ... ... ... ... 83·5 ,, | |
| Total ... ... ... 787 ,, ... | 787 sq. ft. |
| Grate Area ... ... ... ... ... ... ... ... | 13 ,, |
| Working Pressure ... ... ... ... ... ... ... | 160 lbs. per sq. in. |
| Tank Capacity ... ... ... ... ... ... ... ... | 1700 gallons |
| Fuel Space (Wood) ... ... ... ... ... ... ... | 2 tons 0 cwts. |
| Weight Empty (Engine) ... ... ... ... ... ... | 29 ,, 10 ,, |
| ,, ,, (Tender) ... ... ... ... ... ... | 13 ,, 0 ,, |
| Weight in Working Order (Engine) ... ... ... ... ... | 32 ,, 10 ,, |
| ,, ,, ,, (Tender) ... ... ... ... ... | 22 ,, 1 ,, |
| Total Weight of Engine and Tender in Working Order ... ... ... | 54 ,, 11 ,, |
| ,, ,, on Coupled Wheels ... ... ... ... ... | 26 ,, 17 ,, |
| Maximum Axle Load ... ... ... ... ... ... ... | 9 ,, 3 ,, |
| Tractive Effort at 75 per cent. of Boiler Pressure ... ... ... ... | 13500 lbs. |
| Ratio Adhesive Weight ÷ Tractive Effort ... ... ... ... ... | 4·5 |
| Minimum Radius of Curve Engine will traverse with ease ... ... ... | 250 ft. |
| Weight per Yard of Lightest Rail advisable ... ... ... ... | 50 lbs. |
| Load Engine will haul on Level ... ... ... ... ... | 696 tons |
| ,, ,, ,, up Incline of 1 in 100 ... ... ... ... | 338 ,, |
| ,, ,, ,, ,, ,, 1 in 50 ... ... ... ... | 238 ,, |

*Code Word*—**SANMAR**

# THE HUNSLET ENGINE CO. LTD *Engineers* LEEDS ENGLAND

## 0-4-2 TYPE
# SIDE TANK ENGINE

| | |
|---|---|
| Gauge of Railway | 2 ft. 0 in. |
| Size of Cylinders | 7 in. dia. × 12 in. stroke |
| Dia. of Coupled Wheels | 2 ft. 0 in. |
| ,,    Bogie Wheels | 1 ,, 6½ ,, |
| Rigid Wheelbase (Engine) | 3 ,, 6 ,, |
| Total Wheelbase (Engine) | 8 ,, 7 ,, |
| Height from Rail to Top of Chimney | 9 ,, 0 ,, |
| Extreme Width | 6 ,, 1½ ,, |
| Heating Surface—Small Tubes | 139 sq. ft. |
| ,,        ,,     Firebox | 21 ,, |
| Total | 160 ,, |  160 sq. ft. |
| Grate Area | 3·5 ,, |
| Working Pressure | 160 lbs. per sq. in. |
| Tank Capacity | 240 gallons |
| Fuel Space (Coal) | 6½ cwts. |
| Weight Empty (Engine) | 9 tons 5 cwts. |
| ,,    in Working Order (Engine) | 10 ,, 16 ,, |
| Total Weight on Coupled Wheels | 8 ,, 0 ,, |
| Maximum Axle Load | 4 ,, 5 ,, |
| Tractive Effort at 75 per cent. of Boiler Pressure | 2940 lbs. |
| Ratio Adhesive Weight ÷ Tractive Effort | 6·1 |
| Minimum Radius of Curve Engine will traverse with ease | 95 ft. |
| Weight per Yard of Lightest Rail advisable | 25 lbs. |
| Load Engine will haul on Level | 150 tons |
| ,,    ,,    ,,   up incline of 1 in 100 | 75 ,, |
| ,,    ,,    ,,    ,,    ,,   1 in 50 | 40 ,, |

*Code Word*—**BODRY**

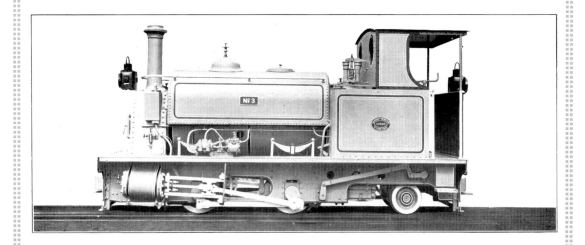

## 0-4-2 TYPE

# SADDLE TANK ENGINE

| | |
|---|---|
| Gauge of Railway | 2 ft. 6 in. |
| Size of Cylinders | 9¼ in. dia. × 14 in. stroke |
| Dia. of Coupled Wheels | 2 ft. 2 in. |
| „ Bogie Wheels | 1 „ 6 „ |
| Rigid Wheelbase (Engine) | 4 „ 6 „ |
| Total Wheelbase (Engine) | 10 „ 3 „ |
| Height from Rail to Top of Chimney | 9 „ 0 „ |
| Extreme Width | 7 „ 0 „ |
| Heating Surface—Small Tubes ... 206 sq. ft. | |
| „ „ Firebox ... 29 „ | |
| Total ... 235 „ | 235 sq. ft. |
| Grate Area | 6·25 „ |
| Working Pressure | 160 lbs. per sq. in. |
| Tank Capacity | 300 gallons |
| Fuel Space (Coal) | 13 cwts. |
| Weight Empty (Engine) | 12 tons 0 cwts. |
| „ in Working Order (Engine) | 14 „ 19 „ |
| Total Weight on Coupled Wheels | 11 „ 17 „ |
| Maximum Axle Load | 5 „ 19 „ |
| Tractive Effort at 75 per cent. of Boiler Pressure | 5528 lbs. |
| Ratio Adhesive Weight ÷ Tractive Effort | 4·8 |
| Minimum Radius of Curve Engine will traverse with ease | 60 ft. |
| Weight per Yard of Lightest Rail advisable | 30 lbs. |
| Load Engine will haul on Level | 290 tons |
| „ „ „ up Incline of 1 in 100 | 145 „ |
| „ „ „ „ „ 1 in 50 | 80 „ |

*Code Word—***SANLU**

## 0-4-0 TYPE

# OIL BURNING TANK ENGINE

| | |
|---|---|
| Gauge of Railway ... ... ... ... ... ... ... ... | 1 ft. 6 in. |
| Size of Cylinders ... ... ... ... ... ... ... ... | 6½ in. dia. × 8 in. stroke |
| Dia. of Coupled Wheels ... ... ... ... ... ... ... | 1 ft. 6½ in. |
| Total Wheelbase (Engine) ... ... ... ... ... ... | 3 ,, 6 ,, |
| Height from Rail to Top of Chimney ... ... ... ... ... | 8 ,, 0 ,, |
| Extreme Width ... ... ... ... ... ... ... | 5 ,, 5 ,, |
| Heating Surface—Small Tubes ... ... ... ... 78 sq. ft. | |
| ,, ,, Firebox ... ... ... ... 18 ,, | |
| Total ... ... ... 96 ,, | 96 sq. ft. |
| Grate Area ... ... ... ... ... ... ... ... ... | 3 ,, |
| Working Pressure ... ... ... ... ... ... ... | 160 lbs. per sq. in. |
| Tank Capacity ... ... ... ... ... ... ... ... | 58 gallons |
| Fuel Space (Oil) ... ... ... ... ... ... ... ... | 25 ,, |
| Weight Empty (Engine) ... ... ... ... ... ... | 5 tons 6 cwts. |
| ,, in Working Order (Engine) ... ... ... ... | 5 ,, 19 ,, |
| Total Weight on Coupled Wheels ... ... ... ... ... | 5 ,, 19 ,, |
| Maximum Axle Load ... ... ... ... ... ... ... | 3 ,, 19 ,, |
| Tractive Effort at 75 per cent. of Boiler Pressure ... ... ... | 2192 lbs. |
| Ratio Adhesive Weight ÷ Tractive Effort ... ... ... ... | 6·1 |
| Minimum Radius of Curve Engine will traverse with ease ... ... ... | 24 ft. |
| Weight per Yard of Lightest Rail advisable ... ... ... ... | 20 lbs. |
| Load Engine will haul on Level ... ... ... ... ... | 115 tons |
| ,, ,, ,, up Incline of 1 in 100 ... ... ... ... ... | 55 ,, |
| ,, ,, ,, ,, ,, 1 in 50 ... ... ... ... ... | 30 ,, |

*Code Word*—**WARIL**

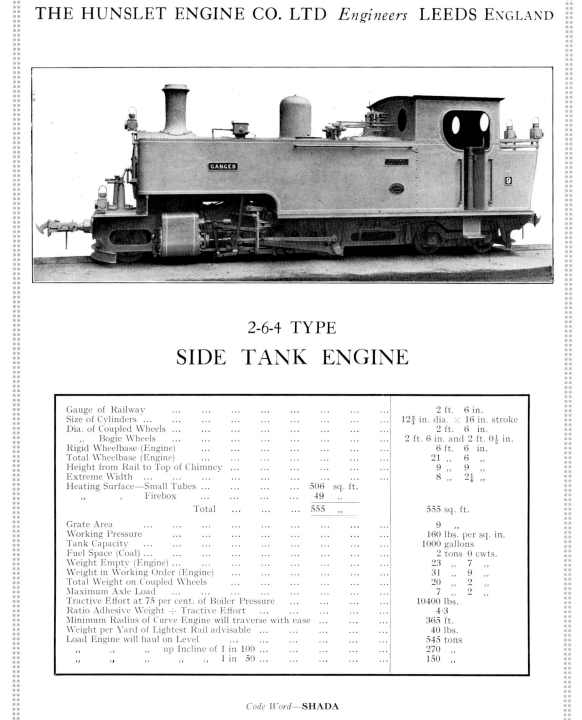

## 2-6-4 TYPE

# SIDE TANK ENGINE

| | |
|---|---|
| Gauge of Railway ... ... ... ... ... ... ... ... | 2 ft. 6 in. |
| Size of Cylinders ... ... ... ... ... ... ... ... | 12¾ in. dia. × 16 in. stroke |
| Dia. of Coupled Wheels ... ... ... ... ... ... ... | 2 ft. 6 in. |
| ,, Bogie Wheels ... ... ... ... ... ... ... | 2 ft. 6 in. and 2 ft. 0½ in. |
| Rigid Wheelbase (Engine) ... ... ... ... ... ... | 6 ft. 6 in. |
| Total Wheelbase (Engine) ... ... ... ... ... ... | 21 ,, 6 ,, |
| Height from Rail to Top of Chimney ... ... ... ... | 9 ,, 9 ,, |
| Extreme Width ... ... ... ... ... ... ... | 8 ,, 2¼ ,, |
| Heating Surface—Small Tubes ... ... ... ... 506 sq. ft. | |
| ,, , Firebox ... ... ... ... 49 ,, | |
| Total ... ... ... 555 ,, | 555 sq. ft. |
| Grate Area ... ... ... ... ... ... ... ... | 9 ,, |
| Working Pressure ... ... ... ... ... ... ... | 160 lbs. per sq. in. |
| Tank Capacity ... ... ... ... ... ... ... | 1000 gallons |
| Fuel Space (Coal) ... ... ... ... ... ... ... | 2 tons 0 cwts. |
| Weight Empty (Engine) ... ... ... ... ... ... | 23 ,, 7 ,, |
| Weight in Working Order (Engine) ... ... ... ... | 31 ,, 9 ,, |
| Total Weight on Coupled Wheels ... ... ... ... | 20 ,, 2 ,, |
| Maximum Axle Load ... ... ... ... ... ... | 7 ,, 2 ,, |
| Tractive Effort at 75 per cent. of Boiler Pressure ... ... | 10400 lbs. |
| Ratio Adhesive Weight ÷ Tractive Effort ... ... ... | 4·3 |
| Minimum Radius of Curve Engine will traverse with ease ... ... | 365 ft. |
| Weight per Yard of Lightest Rail advisable ... ... ... | 40 lbs. |
| Load Engine will haul on Level ... ... ... ... | 545 tons |
| ,, ,, ,, up Incline of 1 in 100 ... ... ... ... | 270 ,, |
| ,, ,, ,, ,, ,, 1 in 50 ... ... ... ... | 150 ,, |

*Code Word—*SHADA

## 4-6-0 TYPE

# SIDE TANK ENGINE

| | |
|---|---|
| Gauge of Railway ... ... ... ... ... ... ... ... | 1 ft. 11⅝ in. (60 cm.) |
| Size of Cylinders ... ... ... ... ... ... ... ... ... | 9½ in. dia. × 12 in. stroke |
| Dia. of Coupled Wheels ... ... ... ... ... ... ... | 2 ft. 0 in. |
| ,,  Bogie Wheels ... ... ... ... ... ... ... | 1 ,, 6½ ,, |
| Rigid Wheelbase (Engine) ... ... ... ... ... ... | 5 ,, 6 ,, |
| Total Wheelbase (Engine) ... ... ... ... ... | 13 ,, 0 ,, |
| Height from Rail to Top of Chimney ... ... ... ... | 8 ,, 11½ ,, |
| Extreme Width ... ... ... ... ... ... | 6 ,, 3½ ,, |
| Heating Surface—Small Tubes ... ... ... ... 168 sq. ft. | |
| ,,  ,, Firebox ... ... ... ... 37 ,, | |
| Total ... ... ... 205 ,, | 205 sq. ft. |
| Grate Area ... ... ... ... ... ... ... ... ... | 3·95 ,, |
| Working Pressure ... ... ... ... ... ... ... | 160 lbs. per sq. in. |
| Tank Capacity ... ... ... ... ... ... ... ... | 375 gallons |
| Fuel Space (Coal) ... ... ... ... ... ... ... | 15 cwts. |
| Weight Empty (Engine) ... ... ... ... ... ... | 10 tons 18 cwts. |
| ,,  in Working Order (Engine) ... ... ... ... | 14 ,, 1 ,, |
| Total Weight on Coupled Wheels ... ... ... ... | 10 ,, 10 ,, |
| Maximum Axle Load ... ... ... ... ... ... | 3 ,, 10 ,, |
| Tractive Effort at 75 per cent. of Boiler Pressure ... ... ... ... | 5415 lbs. |
| Ratio Adhesive Weight ÷ Tractive Effort ... ... ... ... | 4·34 |
| Minimum Radius of Curve Engine will traverse with ease ... ... | 100 ft. |
| Weight per Yard of Lightest Rail advisable ... ... ... ... | 20 lbs. |
| Load Engine will haul on Level ... ... ... ... ... | 286 tons |
| ,,  ,,  ,, up Incline of 1 in 100 ... ... ... ... | 143 ,, |
| ,,  ,,  ,,  ,,  ,, 1 in 50 ... ... ... ... | 80 ,, |

*Code Word*—**WAROFF**

## 0-4-0 TYPE

# SADDLE TANK ENGINE

| | |
|---|---|
| Gauge of Railway ... ... ... ... ... ... ... ... | 3 ft. 0 in. |
| Size of Cylinders ... ... ... ... ... ... ... ... | 9 in. dia. × 14 in. stroke |
| Dia. of Coupled Wheels ... ... ... ... ... ... | 2 ft. 6 in. |
| Total Wheelbase (Engine) ... ... ... ... ... | 4 ,, 6 ,, |
| Height from Rail to Top of Chimney ... ... ... | 9 ,, 0 ,, |
| Extreme Width ... ... ... ... ... ... ... ... | 6 ,, 1½ ,, |
| Heating Surface—Small Tubes ... ... ... ... 184 sq. ft. | |
| ,, ,, Firebox ... ... ... ... 25 ,, | |
| Total ... ... 209 ,, ... | 209 sq. ft. |
| Grate Area ... ... ... ... ... ... ... ... | 4·1 sq. ft. |
| Working Pressure ... ... ... ... ... ... ... | 160 lbs per sq. in. |
| Tank Capacity ... ... ... ... ... ... ... | 240 gallons |
| Fuel Space (Coal) ... ... ... ... ... ... ... | 5 cwts. |
| Weight Empty (Engine) ... ... ... ... ... | 10 tons 4 cwts. |
| ,, in Working Order (Engine) ... ... ... | 12 ,, 8 ,, |
| Total Weight on Coupled Wheels ... ... ... | 12 ,, 8 ,, |
| Maximum Axle Load ... ... ... ... ... ... | 7 ,, 2 ,, |
| Tractive Effort at 75 per cent. of Boiler Pressure ... ... ... ... | 4535 lbs. |
| Ratio Adhesive Weight ÷ Tractive Effort ... ... ... ... | 6 |
| Minimum Radius of Curve Engine will traverse with ease ... ... | 40 ft. |
| Weight per Yard of Lightest Rail advisable ... ... ... ... | 40 lbs. |
| Load Engine will haul on Level ... ... ... ... ... ... | 240 tons |
| ,, ,, ,, up Incline of 1 in 100 ... ... ... ... | 120 ,, |
| ,, ,, ,, ,, ,, 1 in 50 ... ... ... ... | 65 ,, |

*Code Word*—**HAMIL**

## 0-4-0 TYPE

# SADDLE TANK ENGINE

| | |
|---|---|
| Gauge of Railway ... ... ... ... ... ... ... ... | 1 ft. 10¾ in. |
| Size of Cylinders ... ... ... ... ... ... ... ... | 7 in. dia. × 10 in. stroke |
| Dia. of Coupled Wheels ... ... ... ... ... ... ... | 1 ft. 8 in. |
| Rigid Wheelbase (Engine) ... ... ... ... ... ... | 3 ,, 3 ,, |
| Height from Rail to Top of Chimney ... ... ... ... | 7 ,, 3 ,, |
| Extreme Width ... ... ... ... ... ... ... | 5 ,, 4 ,, |
| Heating Surface—Small Tubes ... ... ... ... 86 sq ft. | |
| ,, ,, Firebox ... ... ... ... 14 ,, | |
| Total ... ... ... 100 ,, ... | 100 sq. ft. |
| Grate Area ... ... ... ... ... ... ... ... | 2·5 ,, |
| Working Pressure ... ... ... ... ... ... ... | 160 lbs. per sq. in. |
| Tank Capacity ... ... ... ... ... ... ... | 100 gallons |
| Fuel Space (Coal) ... ... ... ... ... ... ... | 1·5 cwts. |
| Weight Empty (Engine) ... ... ... ... ... | 5 tons 19 cwts |
| ,, in Working Order (Engine) ... ... ... ... | 6 ,, 14 ,, |
| Total Weight on Coupled Wheels ... ... ... ... | 6 ,, 14 ,, |
| Maximum Axle Load ... ... ... ... ... ... | 3 ,, 16 ,, |
| Tractive Effort at 75 per cent. of Boiler Pressure ... ... ... | 2940 lbs. |
| Ratio Adhesive Weight ÷ Tractive Effort ... ... ... ... | 5·1 |
| Minimum Radius of Curve Engine will traverse with ease ... ... | 21 ft. |
| Weight per Yard of Lightest Rail advisable ... ... ... ... | 19 lbs. |
| Load Engine will haul on Level ... ... ... ... ... | 156 tons |
| ,, ,, ,, up Incline of 1 in 100 ... ... ... ... | 77 ,, |
| ,, ,, ,, ,, ,, 1 in 50 ... ... ... ... | 44 ,, |

*Code Word*—**DINOR**

# THE HUNSLET ENGINE CO. LTD *Engineers* LEEDS ENGLAND

## 4-6-0  TYPE

# SIDE  TANK  ENGINE

| | |
|---|---|
| Gauge of Railway | 3 ft.  0 in. |
| Size of Cylinders ... | 15 in. dia. × 20 in. stroke |
| Dia. of Coupled Wheels ... | 3 ft.  9 in. |
| „    Bogie Wheels ... | 2 „  3 „ |
| Rigid Wheelbase (Engine) | 8 „  10 „ |
| Total Wheelbase (Engine) | 19 „  1½ „ |
| Height from Rail to Top of Chimney | 11 „  1⅝ „ |
| Extreme Width ... | 8 „  0 „ |
| Heating Surface—Small Tubes ...      530 sq. ft. | |
| „      „      Firebox ...      74  „ | |
| Total ...      604  „ | 604 sq. ft. |
| Grate Area | 11·5  „ |
| Working Pressure | 160 lbs. per sq. in. |
| Tank Capacity ... | 860 gallons |
| Fuel Space (Coal) | 1 ton 13 cwts. |
| Weight Empty (Engine) | 31 tons 3  „ |
| „  in Working Order (Engine) | 39  „  10  „ |
| Total Weight on Coupled Wheels | 29  „  17  „ |
| Maximum Axle Load | 10  „  4  „ |
| Tractive Effort at 75 per cent. of Boiler Pressure | 12000 lbs. |
| Ratio Adhesive Weight ÷ Tractive Effort | 5·5 |
| Minimum Radius of Curve Engine will traverse with ease | 500 ft. |
| Weight per Yard of Lightest Rail advisable | 50 lbs. |
| Load Engine will haul on Level | 585 tons |
| „      „      „      up incline of 1 in 100 | 300  „ |
| „      „      „      „      „      1 in 50 | 170  „ |

*Code Word—* **TYMON**

## 0-4-0 TYPE

# SADDLE TANK ENGINE

| | |
|---|---|
| Gauge of Railway ... ... ... ... ... ... | 3 ft. 0 in. |
| Size of Cylinders ... ... ... ... ... ... ... | 9 in. dia. × 14 in. stroke |
| Dia. of Coupled Wheels ... ... ... ... ... ... | 2 ft. 6 in. |
| Rigid Wheelbase (Engine) ... ... ... ... ... | 4 ,, 6 ,, |
| Height from Rail to Top of Chimney ... ... ... | 9 ,, 0 ,, |
| Extreme Width ... ... ... ... ... ... | 6 ,, 1½,, |
| Heating Surface—Small Tubes ... ... ... ... 184 sq. ft. | |
| ,, ,, Firebox ... ... ... ... 27·6 ,, | |
| Total ... ... ... 211·6 ,, ... | 211·6 sq. ft. |
| Grate Area ... ... ... ... ... ... ... ... ... | 4·1 ,, |
| Working Pressure ... ... ... ... ... ... ... | 160 lbs per sq. in. |
| Tank Capacity ... ... ... ... ... ... ... | 240 gallons |
| Fuel Space (Coal) ... ... ... ... ... ... | 5 cwts. |
| Weight Empty (Engine) ... ... ... ... ... ... | 10 tons 17 cwts. |
| ,, in Working Order (Engine) ... ... ... ... | 13 ,, 1 ,, |
| Total Weight on Coupled Wheels ... ... ... ... ... | 13 ,, 1 ,, |
| Maximum Axle Load ... ... ... ... ... ... | 7 ,, 6 ,, |
| Tractive Effort at 75 per cent. of Boiler Pressure ... ... ... ... | 4536 lbs. |
| Ratio Adhesive Weight ÷ Tractive Effort ... ... ... ... | 6·4 |
| Minimum Radius of Curve Engine will traverse with ease ... ... | 40 ft. |
| Weight per Yard of Lightest Rail advisable ... ... ... ... | 40 lbs. |
| Load Engine will haul on Level ... ... ... ... ... | 240 tons |
| ,, ,, ,, up Incline of 1 in 100 ... ... ... ... | 120 ,, |
| ,, ,, ,, ,, 1 in 50 ... ... ... ... | 65 ,, |

*Code Word*---**STOCS**

## 2-8-0 TYPE

# TENDER ENGINE (Oil Burner)

| | |
|---|---|
| Gauge of Railway | 2 ft. 6 in. |
| Size of Cylinders | 16½ in. dia. × 20 in. stroke |
| Dia. of Coupled Wheels | 3 ft. 1½ in. |
| „ Bogie Wheels | 2 „ 3 „ |
| „ Tender Wheels | 2 „ 3 „ |
| Rigid Wheelbase (Engine) | 10 „ 7 „ |
| Total Wheelbase (Engine) | 17 „ 1 „ |
| „ „ (Engine and Tender) | 46 „ 2 „ |
| Height from Rail to Top of Chimney | 11 „ 6½ „ |
| Extreme Width | 8 „ 3¼ „ |
| Heating Surface—Small Tubes 1148 sq. ft. | |
| „ „ Firebox 88 „ | |
| Total 1236 „ | 1236 sq. ft. |
| Grate Area | 20·1 „ |
| Working Pressure | 180 lbs. per sq. in. |
| Tank Capacity (Tender) | 3500 gallons |
| Fuel Space (Oil-Tender) | 900 „ |
| Weight Empty (Engine) | 41 tons 15 cwts. |
| „ „ (Tender) | 15 „ 5 „ |
| „ in Working Order (Engine) | 46 „ 16 „ |
| „ „ (Tender) | 34 „ 11 „ |
| Total Weight of Engine and Tender in Working Order | 81 „ 7 „ |
| „ „ „ on Coupled Wheels | 43 „ 6 „ |
| Maximum Axle Load | 10 „ 19 „ |
| Tractive Effort at 75 per cent. of Boiler Pressure | 19600 lbs. |
| Ratio Adhesive Weight ÷ Tractive Effort | 5·0 |
| Minimum Radius of Curve Engine will traverse with ease | 240 ft. |
| Weight per Yard of Lightest Rail advisable | 55 lbs. |
| Load Engine will haul on Level | 1008 tons |
| „ „ „ up Incline of 1 in 100 | 478 „ |
| „ „ „ „ „ 1 in 50 | 262 „ |

*Code Word*—**MIRO**

# THE HUNSLET ENGINE CO. LTD *Engineers* LEEDS ENGLAND

## 4-4-0 TYPE
# SIDE TANK ENGINE

| | |
|---|---|
| Gauge of Railway ... ... ... ... ... ... ... ... | 3 ft. 0 in. |
| Size of Cylinders ... ... ... ... ... ... ... ... | 9 in. dia. × 16 in. stroke |
| Dia. of Coupled Wheels ... ... ... ... ... ... ... | 2 ft. 9 in. |
| ,, Bogie Wheels ... ... ... ... ... ... ... | 1 ,, 8 ,, |
| Rigid Wheelbase (Engine) ... ... ... ... ... ... | 6 ,, 0 ,, |
| Total Wheelbase (Engine) ... ... ... ... ... | 15 ,, 2 ,, |
| Height from Rail to Top of Chimney ... ... ... ... | 10 ,, 8¼ ,, |
| Extreme Width ... ... ... ... ... ... ... ... | 6 ,, 8 ,, |
| Heating Surface—Small Tubes ... ... ... ... 206 sq. ft. | |
| ,, ,, Firebox ... ... ... ... 40 ,, | |
| Total ... ... ... 246 ,, | 246 sq. ft. |
| Grate Area ... ... ... ... ... ... ... ... | 6 ,, |
| Working Pressure ... ... ... ... ... ... ... | 160 lbs. per sq. in. |
| Tank Capacity ... ... ... ... ... ... ... ... | 480 gallons |
| Fuel Space ... ... ... ... ... ... ... ... | |
| Weight Empty (Engine) ... ... ... ... ... ... | 13 tons 11½ cwts. |
| ,, in Working Order (Engine) ... ... ... ... | 17 ,, 6 ,, |
| Total Weight on Coupled Wheels ... ... ... ... | 12 ,, 2 ,, |
| Maximum Axle Load ... ... ... ... ... ... ... | 6 ,, 5 ,, |
| Tractive Effort at **75** per cent. of Boiler Pressure ... ... ... | 4712 lbs. |
| Ratio Adhesive Weight ÷ Tractive Effort ... ... ... ... | 5·75 |
| Minimum Radius of Curve Engine will traverse with ease ... ... | 250 ft. |
| Weight per Yard of Lightest Rail advisable ... ... ... ... | 35 lbs. |
| Load Engine will haul on Level ... ... ... ... ... | 245 tons |
| ,, ,, ,, up Incline of 1 in 100 ... ... ... ... | 120 ,, |
| ,, ,, ,, ,, ,, 1 in 50 ... ... ... ... | 65 ,, |

*Code Word—***SNTMA**

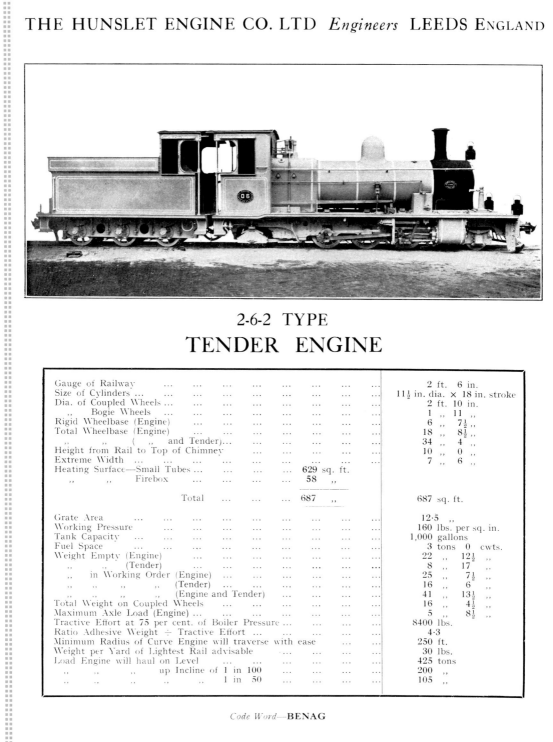

## 2-6-2 TYPE
# TENDER ENGINE

| | |
|---|---|
| Gauge of Railway ... ... ... ... ... ... ... ... | 2 ft. 6 in. |
| Size of Cylinders ... ... ... ... ... ... ... ... | 11½ in. dia. × 18 in. stroke |
| Dia. of Coupled Wheels ... ... ... ... ... ... ... | 2 ft. 10 in. |
| ,, Bogie Wheels ... ... ... ... ... ... ... | 1 ,, 11 ,, |
| Rigid Wheelbase (Engine) ... ... ... ... ... ... | 6 ,, 7½ ,, |
| Total Wheelbase (Engine) ... ... ... ... ... ... | 18 ,, 8½ ,, |
| ,, ,, ( ,, and Tender)... ... ... ... ... ... | 34 ,, 4 ,, |
| Height from Rail to Top of Chimney ... ... ... ... | 10 ,, 0 ,, |
| Extreme Width ... ... ... ... ... ... ... | 7 ,, 6 ,, |
| Heating Surface—Small Tubes ... ... ... ... 629 sq. ft. | |
| ,, ,, Firebox ... ... ... 58 ,, | |
| Total ... ... ... 687 ,, | 687 sq. ft. |
| Grate Area ... ... ... ... ... ... ... ... | 12·5 ,, |
| Working Pressure ... ... ... ... ... ... ... | 160 lbs. per sq. in. |
| Tank Capacity ... ... ... ... ... ... ... | 1,000 gallons |
| Fuel Space ... ... ... ... ... ... ... ... | 3 tons 0 cwts. |
| Weight Empty (Engine) ... ... ... ... ... ... | 22 ,, 12½ ,, |
| ,, ,, (Tender) ... ... ... ... ... ... | 8 ,, 17 ,, |
| ,, in Working Order (Engine) ... ... ... ... ... | 25 ,, 7½ ,, |
| ,, ,, ,, (Tender) ... ... ... ... ... | 16 ,, 6 ,, |
| ,, ,, ,, ,, (Engine and Tender) ... ... ... | 41 ,, 13½ ,, |
| Total Weight on Coupled Wheels ... ... ... ... | 16 ,, 4½ ,, |
| Maximum Axle Load (Engine) ... ... ... ... ... | 5 ,, 8½ ,, |
| Tractive Effort at 75 per cent. of Boiler Pressure ... ... | 8400 lbs. |
| Ratio Adhesive Weight ÷ Tractive Effort ... ... ... ... | 4·3 |
| Minimum Radius of Curve Engine will traverse with ease ... ... | 250 ft. |
| Weight per Yard of Lightest Rail advisable ... ... ... ... | 30 lbs. |
| Load Engine will haul on Level ... ... ... ... ... | 425 tons |
| ,, ,, ,, up Incline of 1 in 100 ... ... ... ... | 200 ,, |
| ,, ,, ,, ,, ,, 1 in 50 ... ... ... ... | 105 ,, |

*Code Word*—**BENAG**

## 0-6-4 TYPE

# SIDE  TANK  ENGINE

| | |
|---|---|
| Gauge of Railway | 2 ft. 6 in. |
| Size of Cylinders | 10 in. dia. × 15 in. stroke |
| Dia. of Coupled Wheels | 2 ft. 3  in. |
| ,,     Bogie Wheels | 1  ,,  9 |
| Rigid Wheelbase | 5  ,,  6  ,, |
| Total Wheelbase | 14  ,,  0  ,, |
| Height from Rail to Top of Chimney | 9  ,,  8 11/16  ,, |
| Extreme Width | 7  ,,  0½  ,, |
| Heating Surface—Small Tubes | 302 sq. ft. |
| ,,      ,,      Firebox | 43  ,, |
| Total | 345  ,,   345 sq. ft. |
| Grate Area | 8·75  ,, |
| Working Pressure | 160 lbs. per sq. in. |
| Tank Capacity | 600 gallons |
| Fuel Space (Wood) | 17 cwts. |
| Weight Empty | 14 tons 19 cwts. |
| ,,  in Working Order | 19  ,,  15  ,, |
| Total Weight on Coupled Wheels | 12  ,,  15  ,, |
| Maximum Axle Load | 4  ,,  9  ,, |
| Tractive Effort at 75 per cent. of Boiler Pressure | 6667 lbs. |
| Ratio Adhesive Weight ÷ Tractive Effort | 4·3 |
| Minimum Radius of Curve Engine will traverse with ease | 135 ft. |
| Weight per Yard of Lightest Rail advisable | 25 lbs. |
| Load Engine will haul on Level | 350 tons |
| ,,   ,,   ,,   up Incline of 1 in 100 | 175  ,, |
| ,,   ,,   ,,   ,,   ,,   1 in 50 | 95  ,, |

*Code Word—***KBENG**

## 0-6-0 TYPE

# SIDE TANK LOCOMOTIVE

| | |
|---|---|
| Gauge of Railway (can be modified to suit requirements) ... ... ... | 2 ft. 0 in. |
| Size of Cylinders ... ... ... ... ... ... ... ... | 8½ in. dia. × 12 in. stroke |
| Dia. of Coupled Wheels ... ... ... ... ... ... ... | 2 ft. 0 ,, |
| Rigid Wheelbase ... ... ... ... ... ... ... ... | 4 ,, 6 ,, |
| Height from Rail to Top of Chimney ... ... ... ... ... | 9 ,, 4 ,, |
| Width Overall ... ... ... ... ... ... ... ... | 6 ,, 4 ,, |
| Heating Surface—Small Tubes ... ... 161 sq. ft. ... ... ... | |
| ,,    ,,    Firebox ... ... 26 ,, ,, ... ... | |
| Total 187 ,, ,, ... ... ... | 187 sq. ft. |
| Grate Area ... ... ... ... ... ... ... ... ... | 5·5 ,, |
| Working Pressure ... ... ... ... ... ... ... ... | 160 lbs. per sq. in. |
| Tank Capacity ... ... ... ... ... ... ... ... | 220 gallons |
| Fuel Space ... ... ... ... ... ... ... ... ... | 4 cwts. |
| Weight Empty ... ... ... ... ... ... ... ... | 9 tons 5 cwt. |
| ,, in Working Order ... ... ... ... ... ... ... | 11 ,, 6 ,, |
| Maximum Axle Load ... ... ... ... ... ... ... | 4 ,, 11 ,, |
| Tractive Effort at 75 per cent of Boiler Pressure ... ... ... ... | 4,335 lbs. |
| Ratio. Adhesive Weight ÷ Tractive Effort ... ... ... ... | 5·9 to 1 |
| Minimum Radius of Curve Engine will traverse with ease ... ... ... | 50 ft. |
| Weight per Yard of Lightest Rail advisable ... ... ... ... | 25 lbs. |
| Load Engine will haul on Level ... ... ... ... ... | 230 tons |
| ,, ,, ,, ,, up Incline of 1 in 100 ... ... ... ... | 115 ,, |
| ,, ,, ,, ,, ,, ,, 1 in 50 ... ... ... ... | 65 ,, |

Loads hauled are based on 18 lbs./ton Starting Resistance on Level and 12 lbs./ton Running Resistance up Inclines.

*Code Word—***AFZEB**

## 2-6-2 TYPE
# SIDE TANK LOCOMOTIVE

| | |
|---|---|
| Gauge of Railway (can be modified to suit requirements) ... ... ... | 2 ft. 6 in. |
| Size of Cylinders ... ... ... ... ... ... ... ... | 10¾ in. dia. × 15 in. stroke |
| Dia. of Coupled Wheels ... ... ... ... ... ... ... | 2 ft. 4 in. |
| „ Bogie Wheels ... ... ... ... ... ... ... | 1 „ 6 „ |
| Rigid Wheelbase ... ... ... ... ... ... ... | 5 „ 6 „ |
| Total Wheelbase ... ... ... ... ... ... ... | 15 „ 4 „ |
| Height Overall ... ... ... ... ... ... ... | 10 „ 5⅝ „ |
| Width Overall ... ... ... ... ... ... ... | 7 „ 5 „ |
| Length over buffer beams ... ... ... ... ... ... | 18 „ 10 „ |
| Heating Surface—Small Tubes ... ... ... ... 345 sq. ft. | |
| „ „ Firebox ... ... ... 36 „ „ | |
| Total ... ... 381 „ „ | 381 sq. ft. |
| Grate Area ... ... ... ... ... ... ... ... | 6¼ „ „ |
| Working Pressure ... ... ... ... ... ... ... | 160 lbs. per sq. in. |
| Tank Capacity ... ... ... ... ... ... ... | 470 gallons |
| Fuel Space (Coal) ... ... ... ... ... ... ... | 1 ton |
| Weight Empty ... ... ... ... ... ... ... | 16 tons 18 cwt. |
| „ in Working Order ... ... ... ... ... ... | 21 „ 5 „ |
| Total Weight on Coupled Wheels ... ... ... ... ... | 13 „ 0 „ |
| Maximum Axle Load ... ... ... ... ... ... ... | 4 „ 10 „ |
| Tractive Effort at 75 per cent. of Boiler Pressure ... ... ... | 7,450 lbs. |
| Ratio Adhesive Weight ÷ Tractive Effort ... ... ... ... | 3·94 to 1 |
| Minimum Radius of Curve of Railway ... ... ... ... ... | 132 ft. |
| Weight per Yard of Lightest Rail advisable ... ... ... ... | 25 lbs. |
| Load Engine will haul on Level ... ... ... ... ... | 390 tons |
| „ „ „ „ up incline of 1 in 100 ... ... ... ... | 195 „ |
| „ „ „ „ „ „ „ 1 in 50 ... ... ... ... | 110 „ |

Loads hauled are based on 18 lbs./ton Starting Resistance on level and 12 lbs./ton Running Resistance up inclines

*Code Word—**SLEON***

# THE HUNSLET ENGINE CO. LTD *Engineers* LEEDS ENGLAND

## 0-6-2 TYPE
# SIDE TANK LOCOMOTIVE

| | |
|---|---|
| Gauge of Railway (can be modified to suit requirements) ... ... ... | 2 ft.  0 ¼  in. |
| Size of Cylinders ... ... ... ... ... ... ... ... | 10¾ in. dia. × 15 in. stroke |
| Dia. of Coupled Wheels ... ... ... ... ... ... ... | 2 ft.  6  in. |
| ,,  Bogie Wheels ... ... ... ... ... ... ... | 1 ,,  6  ,, |
| Rigid Wheelbase ... ... ... ... ... ... ... | 5 ,,  10  ,, |
| Total Wheelbase ... ... ... ... ... ... ... | 11 ,,  8  ,, |
| Height from Rail to Top of Chimney ... ... ... ... | 9 ,,  5½  ,, |
| Width Overall ... ... ... ... ... ... ... ... | 7 ,,  1¼  ,, |
| Heating Surface—Small Tubes ... ... ... ... 337 sq. ft. | |
| ,,  ,,  Firebox ... ... ... ... ... 37 ,, | |
| Total ... ... 374 ,, | 374 square feet |
| Grate Area ... ... ... ... ... ... ... ... | 7·1 ,, |
| Working Pressure ... ... ... ... ... ... ... | 180 lbs. per sq. in. |
| Tank Capacity ... ... ... ... ... ... ... ... | 460 gallons |
| Fuel Space ... ... ... ... ... ... ... ... | 16 cwts. |
| Weight Empty ... ... ... ... ... ... ... | 16 tons 9 cwts. |
| ,, in Working Order ... ... ... ... ... ... | 20 ,,  11 ,, |
| Total Weight on Coupled Wheels ... ... ... ... | 17 ,,  5 ,, |
| Maximum Axle Load ... ... ... ... ... ... ... | 5 ,, 17 ,, |
| Tractive Effort at 75 per cent. of Boiler Pressure ... ... ... | 7,820 lbs. |
| Ratio. Adhesive Weight ÷ Tractive Effort ... ... ... ... | 4·94 to 1 |
| Minimum Radius of Curve Engine will traverse with ease ... ... | 100 ft. |
| Weight per Yard of Lightest Rail advisable ... ... ... ... | 35 lbs. |
| Load Engine will haul on Level ... ... ... ... ... | 415 tons |
| ,,  ,,  ,, up Incline of 1 in 100 ... ... ... ... | 205 ,, |
| ,,  ,,  ,, ,, ,, 1 in 50 ... ... ... ... | 115 ,, |

Loads hauled are based on 18 lbs./ton Starting Resistance on level and 12 lbs./ton Running Resistance up inclines

*Code Word—* **NALTA**

2-8-4 TYPE

# SIDE TANK ENGINE

| | |
|---|---|
| Gauge of Railway ... ... ... ... ... ... ... ... | 2 ft. 6 in. |
| Size of Cylinders ... ... ... ... ... ... ... ... | 12 in. dia. × 18 in. stroke |
| Dia. of Coupled Wheels ... ... ... ... ... ... ... | 2 ft. 9 in. |
| ,, Bogie Wheels ... ... ... ... ... ... ... | 1 ,, 9 ,, |
| Rigid Wheelbase (Engine) ... ... ... ... ... | 9 ,, 9 ,, |
| Total Wheelbase (Engine) ... ... ... ... ... | 26 ,, 0 ,, |
| Height from Rail to Top of Chimney ... ... ... ... | 10 ,, 0 ,, |
| Extreme Width ... ... ... ... ... ... ... ... | 7 ,, 6 ,, |
| Heating Surface—Small Tubes ... ... ... ... 575 sq. ft. | |
| ,, ,, Firebox ... ... ... ... 52 ,, | |
| Total ... ... ... 627 ,, | 627 sq. ft. |
| Grate Area ... ... ... ... ... ... ... ... | 12 ,, |
| Working Pressure ... ... ... ... ... ... ... | 175 lbs. per sq. in. |
| Tank Capacity ... ... ... ... ... ... ... ... | 900 gallons |
| Fuel Space (Coal) ... ... ... ... ... ... ... | 3 tons 0 cwts. |
| Weight Empty (Engine) ... ... ... ... ... ... | 27 ,, 16 ,, |
| Weight in Working Order (Engine) ... ... ... ... | 37 ,, 8 ,, |
| Total Weight on Coupled Wheels ... ... ... ... | 21 ,, 16 ,, |
| Maximum Axle Load ... ... ... ... ... ... | 5 ,, 10 ,, |
| Tractive Effort at 75 per cent. of Boiler Pressure ... ... ... | 10310 lbs. |
| Ratio Adhesive Weight ÷ Tractive Effort ... ... ... ... | 4·74 |
| Minimum Radius of Curve Engine will traverse with ease ... ... | 230 ft. |
| Weight per Yard of Lightest Rail advisable ... ... ... ... | 30 lbs. |
| Load Engine will haul on Level ... ... ... ... ... | 535 tons |
| ,, ,, ,, up Incline of 1 in 100 ... ... ... ... | 262 ,, |
| ,, ,, ,, ,, ,, 1 in 50 ... ... ... ... | 144 ,, |

*Code Word—***DOLPH**

## 0-6-2 TYPE

# SIDE TANK LOCOMOTIVE

| | |
|---|---|
| Gauge of Railway | 2 ft. 6 in. |
| Size of Cylinders | 10½ in. dia. × 16 in. stroke |
| Dia. of Coupled Wheels | 2 ft. 9 in. |
| ,, Bogie Wheels | 2 ,, 1 ,, |
| Rigid Wheelbase | 6 ,, 2 ,, |
| Total Wheelbase | 12 ,, 5 ,, |
| Height from Rail to Top of Chimney | 9 ,, 8 $\frac{9}{16}$ ,, |
| Width Overall ... | 7 ,, 5 ,, |
| Heating Surface—Small Tubes | 322 sq. ft. |
| ,, ,, Firebox | 45 ,, |
| Total | 367 ,,     367 square feet |
| Grate Area | 9·75 ,, |
| Working Pressure | 160 lbs. per sq. in. |
| Tank Capacity ... | 550 gallons |
| Fuel Space | 25 cwts. |
| Weight Empty ... | 18 tons 15 cwts. |
| ,, in Working Order ... | 24 ,, 5 ,, |
| Total Weight on Coupled Wheels | 17 ,, 16 ,, |
| Maximum Axle Load | 6 ,, 10 ,, |
| Tractive Effort at 75 per cent. of Boiler Pressure | 6,413 lbs. |
| Ratio. Adhesive Weight ÷ Tractive Effort | 6·2 to 1 |
| Minimum Radius of Curve Engine will traverse with ease | 120 ft. |
| Weight per Yard of Lightest Rail advisable | 35 lbs. |
| Load Engine will haul on Level | 330 tons |
| ,, ,, ,, up Incline of 1 in 100 | 160 ,, |
| ,, ,, ,, ,, ,, 1 in 50 | 90 ,, |

Loads hauled are based on 18 lbs./ton Starting Resistance on level and 12 lbs./ton Running Resistance up inclines

*Code Word—***NEPAL**

# THE HUNSLET ENGINE CO. LTD *Engineers* LEEDS ENGLAND

## 0-4-2 TYPE

# SADDLE TANK LOCOMOTIVE

| | |
|---|---|
| Gauge of Railway (can be modified to suit requirements) ... ... ... | 2 ft. 0 in. |
| Size of Cylinders ... ... ... ... ... ... ... ... ... | 8 in. dia. × 12 in. stroke |
| Dia. of Coupled Wheels ... ... ... ... ... ... ... | 2 ft. 3 in. |
| ,, Bogie Wheels ... ... ... ... ... ... ... | 1 ,, 4½ ,, |
| Rigid Wheelbase ... ... ... ... ... ... ... ... | 3 ,, 0 ,, |
| Total Wheelbase ... ... ... ... ... ... ... ... | 7 ,, 11 ,, |
| Height from Rail to Top of Chimney ... ... ... ... | 9 ,, 0 3/16 ,, |
| Width Overall ... ... ... ... ... ... ... ... ... | 6 ,, 7 ,, |
| Heating Surface—Small Tubes ... ... ... 127 sq. ft. | |
| ,, ,, Firebox ... ... ... 25 ,, | |
| Total ... ... ... 152 ,, | 152 sq. ft. |
| Grate Area ... ... ... ... ... ... ... ... | 5 ,, |
| Working Pressure ... ... ... ... ... ... ... | 160 lbs. per sq. in. |
| Tank Capacity ... ... ... ... ... ... ... ... | 250 gallons |
| Fuel Space ... ... ... ... ... ... ... ... | 14 cwts. |
| Weight Empty ... ... ... ... ... ... ... ... | 8 tons 0 cwts. |
| ,, in Working Order ... ... ... ... ... ... | 10 ,, 2 ,, |
| Total Weight on Coupled Wheels ... ... ... ... ... | 7 ,, 4 ,, |
| Maximum Axle Load ... ... ... ... ... ... ... | 3 ,, 15 ,, |
| Tractive Effort at 75 per cent. of Boiler Pressure ... ... | 3,415 lbs. |
| Ratio Adhesive Weight ÷ Tractive Effort ... ... ... ... | 5·20 to 1 |
| Minimum Radius of Curve Engine will traverse with ease ... ... | 50 ft. |
| Weight per Yard of Lightest Rail advisable ... ... ... | 20 lbs. |
| Load Engine will haul on Level ... ... ... ... ... | 180 tons |
| ,, ,, ,, up Incline of 1 in 100 ... ... ... | 90 ,, |
| ,, ,, ,, ,, ,, 1 in 50 ... ... ... | 50 ,, |

Loads hauled are based on 18 lbs./ton starting resistance on level and 12 lbs./ton running resistance up inclines

*Code Word—***DAWIN**

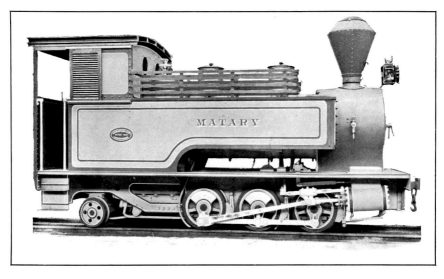

## 0-6-2 TYPE

# SIDE TANK LOCOMOTIVE

| | |
|---|---|
| Gauge of Railway (can be modified to suit requirements) ... ... ... | Metre |
| Size of Cylinders ... ... ... ... ... ... ... ... ... | 10 in. dia. × 15 in. stroke |
| Dia. of Coupled Wheels ... ... ... ... ... ... ... | 2 ft. 3 in. |
| ,, Bogie Wheels ... ... ... ... ... ... ... | 1 ,, 6 ,, |
| Rigid Wheelbase ... ... ... ... ... ... ... ... | 5 ,, 6 ,, |
| Total Wheelbase ... ... ... ... ... ... ... | 11 ,, 6 ,, |
| Height from Rail to Top of Chimney ... ... ... ... | 10 ,, 7⅞ ,, |
| Width Overall ... ... ... ... ... ... ... ... | 7 ,, 4 ,, |
| Heating Surface—Small Tubes ... ... ... 272 sq. ft. | |
| ,, ,, Firebox ... ... ... ... 42 ,, | |
| Total ... ... ... 314 ,, | 314 sq. ft. |
| Grate Area ... ... ... ... ... ... ... ... | 6·5 ,, |
| Working Pressure ... ... ... ... ... ... ... | 160 lbs. per sq. in |
| Tank Capacity ... ... ... ... ... ... ... ... | 420 gallons |
| Fuel Space ... ... ... ... ... ... ... ... | 15 cwts. |
| Weight Empty ... ... ... ... ... ... ... ... | 12 tons 16 cwts. |
| ,, in Working Order ... ... ... ... ... ... | 16 ,, 15 ,, |
| Total Weight on Coupled Wheels ... ... ... ... | 13 ,, 11 ,, |
| Maximum Axle Load ... ... ... ... ... ... | 4 ,, 11 ,, |
| Tractive Effort at 75 per cent. of Boiler Pressure ... ... ... | 6,670 lbs. |
| Ratio Adhesive Weight ÷ Tractive Effort ... ... ... ... | 4·55 to 1 |
| Minimum Radius of Curve Engine will traverse with ease ... ... | 90 ft. |
| Weight per Yard of Lightest Rail advisable ... ... ... ... | 25 lbs. |
| Load Engine will haul on Level ... ... ... ... ... | 355 tons |
| ,, ,, ,, up Incline of 1 in 100 ... ... ... ... | 180 ,, |
| ,, ,, ,, ,, ,, 1 in 50 ... ... ... ... | 100 ,, |

Loads hauled are based on 18 lbs./ton starting resistance on level and 12 lbs./ton running resistance up inclines

*Code Word*—**MATRY**

## 0-4-0+0-4-0 TYPE
# ARTICULATED GEARED LOCOMOTIVE

| | | |
|---|---|---|
| Gauge of Railway (can be modified to suit requirements) ... ... ... | | 2 ft. 0 in. |
| Size of Cylinders ... ... ... ... ... ... ... ... ... | | 6½ in. dia. × 8 in. stroke |
| Number of Cylinders ... ... ... ... ... ... ... ... | | Four |
| Dia. of Coupled Wheels ... ... ... ... ... ... ... ... | | 2 ft. 0 in. |
| Rigid Wheelbase ... ... ... ... ... ... ... ... | | 3 ,, 6 ,, |
| Total Wheelbase ... ... ... ... ... ... ... ... | | 19 ,, 0 ,, |
| Height from Rail to Top of Chimney ... ... ... ... ... | | 10 ,, 10⅛ ,, |
| Width Overall ... ... ... ... ... ... ... ... | | 7 ,, 3 ,, |
| Heating Surface—Small Tubes ... ... ... ... | 157 sq. ft. | |
| ,, ,, Large Tubes ... ... ... ... | 93 ,, | |
| ,, ,, Firebox ... ... ... ... | 41 ,, | |
| ,, ,, Total ... ... ... | 291 ,, | 291 sq. ft. |
| ,, ,, Superheater Elements ... ... | 70 ,, | |
| ,, ,, Total ... ... ... | 361 ,, | 361 sq. ft. |
| Grate Area ... ... ... ... ... ... ... ... | | 9·8 ,, |
| Working Pressure ... ... ... ... ... ... ... ... | | 185 lbs. per sq. in. |
| Tank Capacity ... ... ... ... ... ... ... ... | | 500 gallons |
| Fuel Space ... ... ... ... ... ... ... ... | | 14 cwts. |
| Weight Empty ... ... ... ... ... ... ... ... | | 20 tons 8 cwts. |
| ,, in Working Order ... ... ... ... ... ... | | 25 ,, 1 ,, |
| Maximum Axle Load ... ... ... ... ... ... ... | | 6 ,, 10 ,, |
| Tractive Effort at 75 per cent. of Boiler Pressure ... ... ... | | 12,375 lbs. |
| Ratio Adhesive Weight ÷ Tractive Effort ... ... ... | | 4·5 to 1 |
| Minimum Radius of Curve Engine will traverse with ease ... ... | | 60 ft. |
| Weight per Yard of Lightest Rail advisable ... ... ... ... | | 35 lbs. |
| Load Engine will haul on Level ... ... ... ... ... | | 660 tons |
| ,, ,, ,, up Incline of 1 in 100 ... ... ... ... | | 335 ,, |
| ,, ,, ,, ,, ,, 1 in 50 ... ... ... ... | | 190 ,, |

Loads hauled are based on 18 lbs./ton starting resistance on level and 12 lbs./ton running resistance up inclines

*Code Word*—**AFOUR**

## 0-4-2 TYPE

# SIDE TANK LOCOMOTIVE

| | |
|---|---|
| Gauge of Railway (can be modified to suit requirements) ... ... ... | 2 ft. 0 in. |
| Size of Cylinders ... ... ... ... ... ... ... ... ... | 9¼ in. dia. × 14 in. stroke |
| Dia. of Coupled Wheels ... ... ... ... ... ... ... ... | 2 ft. 3 in. |
| „ Bogie Wheels ... ... ... ... ... ... ... ... | 1 „ 7 „ |
| Rigid Wheelbase ... ... ... ... ... ... ... ... ... | 4 „ 0 „ |
| Total Wheelbase ... ... ... ... ... ... ... ... ... | 9 „ 6 „ |
| Height from Rail to Top of Chimney ... ... ... ... ... ... | 9 „ 4 3/16 „ |
| Width Overall ... ... ... ... ... ... ... ... ... | 6 „ 8 „ |
| Heating Surface—Small Tubes ... ... ... ... 217 sq. ft. | |
| „ „ Firebox ... ... ... ... 27 „ | |
| Total ... ... ... 244 „ | 244 square feet |
| Grate Area ... ... ... ... ... ... ... ... ... | 6·3 „ |
| Working Pressure ... ... ... ... ... ... ... ... | 180 lbs. per sq. in. |
| Tank Capacity ... ... ... ... ... ... ... ... ... | 400 gallons |
| Fuel Space ... ... ... ... ... ... ... ... ... | 15 cwts. |
| Weight Empty ... ... ... ... ... ... ... ... ... | 11 tons 13 cwts. |
| „ in Working Order ... ... ... ... ... ... ... | 15 „ 7 „ |
| Total Weight on Coupled Wheels ... ... ... ... ... ... | 12 „ 1 „ |
| Maximum Axle Load ... ... ... ... ... ... ... ... | 6 „ 1 „ |
| Tractive Effort at 75 per cent. of Boiler Pressure ... ... ... ... | 5,990 lbs. |
| Ratio Adhesive Weight ÷ Tractive Effort ... ... ... ... ... | 4·5 to 1 |
| Minimum Radius of Curve Engine will traverse with ease ... ... ... | 70 ft. |
| Weight per Yard of Lightest Rail advisable ... ... ... ... ... | 30 lbs. |
| Load Engine will haul on Level ... ... ... ... ... ... | 320 tons |
| „ „ „ up Incline of 1 in 100 ... ... ... ... ... | 160 „ |
| „ „ „ „ „ 1 in 50 ... ... ... ... ... | 90 „ |

Loads hauled are based on 18 lbs./ton Starting Resistance on level and 12 lbs./ton Running Resistance up inclines

*Code Word*—**ANHEJ**

## 0-4-2 TYPE
# SIDE TANK LOCOMOTIVE

| | |
|---|---|
| Gauge of Railway (can be modified to suit requirements) ... ... ... | 2 ft. 0 in. |
| Size of Cylinders ... ... ... ... ... ... ... ... ... | 7 ins. dia. × 10 in. stroke |
| Dia. of Coupled Wheels ... ... ... ... ... ... ... ... | 1 ft. 8 in. |
| ,, Bogie Wheels ... ... ... ... ... ... ... ... | 1 ,, 3 ,, |
| Rigid Wheelbase ... ... ... ... ... ... ... ... ... | 3 ,, 6 ,, |
| Total Wheelbase ... ... ... ... ... ... ... ... | 6 ,, 9 ,, |
| Height from Rail to Top of Chimney ... ... ... ... ... | 9 ,, 0 ,, |
| Width Overall ... ... ... ... ... ... ... ... | 5 ,, 10 ,, |
| Heating Surface—Small Tubes ... ... ... ... 106 sq. ft. | |
| ,, ,, Firebox ... ... ... ... 22 ,, | |
| Total ... ... ... 128 ,, | 128 square feet |
| Grate Area ... ... ... ... ... ... ... ... ... | 4·7 ,, |
| Working Pressure ... ... ... ... ... ... ... ... | 160 lbs. per sq. in. |
| Tank Capacity ... ... ... ... ... ... ... ... ... | 200 gallons |
| Fuel Space ... ... ... ... ... ... ... ... ... | 7 cwts. |
| Weight Empty ... ... ... ... ... ... ... ... ... | 7 tons 0 cwts. |
| ,, in Working Order ... ... ... ... ... ... ... | 8 ,, 12 ,, |
| Total Weight on Coupled Wheels ... ... ... ... ... | 6 ,, 5 ,, |
| Maximum Axle Load ... ... ... ... ... ... ... ... | 3 ,, 5 ,, |
| Tractive Effort at 75 per cent. of Boiler Pressure ... ... ... ... | 2,940 lbs. |
| Ratio Adhesive Weight ÷ Tractive Effort ... ... ... ... ... | 4·75 to 1 |
| Minimum Radius of Curve Engine will traverse with ease ... ... ... | 55 ft. |
| Weight per Yard of Lightest Rail advisable ... ... ... ... ... | 18 lbs. |
| Load Engine will haul on Level ... ... ... ... ... ... | 155 tons |
| ,, ,, ,, up Incline of 1 in 100 ... ... ... ... ... | 75 ,, |
| ,, ,, ,, ,, 1 in 50 ... ... ... ... ... | 45 ,, |

Loads hauled are based on 18 lbs./ton Starting Resistance on level and 12 lbs./ton Running Resistance up inclines

*Code Word*—**ANDIE**

0-4-0+0-4-0 TYPE

# 75 H.P. "HUNSLET" ARTICULATED DIESEL LOCOMOTIVE

| | | |
|---|---|---|
| Gauge of Railway ... | ... | 1 ft. 6 in. |
| Dia. of Coupled Wheels ... | ... | 1 ,, 8 ,, |
| Bogie Wheelbase ... | ... | 3 ,, 0 ,, |
| Total Wheelbase ... | ... | 12 ,, 0 ,, |
| Height Overall ... | ... | 9 ,, 0 ,, |
| Width Overall ... | ... | 5 ,, 1½ ,, |
| Length over Buffer Beams ... | ... | 18 ,, 1¼ ,, |
| Number of Speeds ... | ... | 2 forward, 2 reverse |
| Maximum Speed ... | ... | 8·8 miles per hour |
| Normal Speed 1st Gear ... | ... | 4 ,, ,, |
| ,, ,, 2nd Gear ... | ... | 8 ,, ,, |
| Fuel Capacity ... | ... | 60 gallons |
| Weight in Working Order ... | ... | 13 tons 5 cwts. |
| Maximum Axle Load ... | ... | 3 ,, 19 ,, |
| ,, Tractive Effort ... | ... | 6,570 lb. |
| Normal Tractive Effort, 1st Gear ... | ... | 5,980 ,, |
| ,, ,, ,, 2nd Gear ... | ... | 2,990 ,, |
| Ratio. Adhesive Weight ÷ Tractive Effort ... | ... | 4·5 |
| Minimum Radius of Curve Engine will traverse with ease ... | ... | 30 ft. |
| Weight per Yard of Lightest Rail advisable ... | ... | 20 lb. |

| | Level | 1 in 100 | 1 in 50 |
|---|---|---|---|
| Load Engine will start and haul in 1st Gear ... | 352 tons | 150 tons | 91 tons |
| ,, ,, ,, haul in 2nd Gear ... | 236 ,, | 74 ,, | 40 ,, |

NOTE—The Locomotive is capable of delivering 82 h.p. for short periods

*Code Word*—**ARTIC**

# THE HUNSLET ENGINE CO. LTD *Engineers* LEEDS ENGLAND

## 0-6-0 TYPE
# 100 H.P. "HUNSLET" DIESEL LOCOMOTIVE
## FOR UNDERGROUND WORKING

| | | |
|---|---|---|
| Gauge of Railway (can be modified to suit requirements) ... ... ... | 2 ft. 6 in. | |
| Dia. of Coupled Wheels ... ... ... ... ... ... ... | 2 ,, 0 ,, | |
| Wheelbase ... ... ... ... ... ... ... ... | 5 ,, 3 ,, | |
| Height Overall ... ... ... ... ... ... ... ... | 5 ,, 4 ,, | |
| Width Overall ... ... ... ... ... ... ... ... | 3 ,, 11 ,, | |
| Length Overall ... ... ... ... ... ... ... ... | 15 ,, 8 ,, | |
| Length over Buffer Beam Faces ... ... ... ... ... | 14 ,, 3 ,, | |
| Maximum Power and Speed of Engine ... ... ... ... | 100 h.p. at 1,700 r.p.m. | |
| Speed 1st Gear ... ... ... ... ... ... ... | 4 miles per hour | |
| ,, 2nd Gear ... ... ... ... ... ... ... | 6·1 ,, ,, ,, | |
| ,, 3rd Gear ... ... ... ... ... ... ... | 9·4 ,, ,, ,, | |
| ,, 4th Gear ... ... ... ... ... ... ... | 14·6 ,, ,, ,, | |
| Fuel Capacity ... ... ... ... ... ... ... | 18 gallons | |
| Weight in Working Order ... ... ... ... ... ... | 15 tons 0 cwts. | |
| Maximum Axle Load ... ... ... ... ... ... ... | 5 ,, 5 ,, | |
| Maximum Tractive Effort 1st Gear ... ... ... ... ... | 8000 lbs. | |
| Tractive Effort 2nd Gear ... ... ... ... ... | 5,200 lbs. | |
| ,, ,, 3rd Gear ... ... ... ... ... | 3,400 lbs. | |
| ,, ,, 4th Gear ... ... ... ... ... | 2,200 lbs. | |
| Ratio. Adhesive Weight ÷ Tractive Effort ... ... ... ... | 4·2 to 1 | |
| Minimum Radius of Curve Locomotive will traverse without train ... ... | 60 ft. | |
| Weight per Yard of Lightest Rail advisable ... ... ... ... | 28 lbs. | |

| | Level | 1 in 100 | 1 in 50 |
|---|---|---|---|
| Load Engine will start and haul in 1st Gear ... ... ... ... | 430 tons | 180 tons | 110 tons |
| ,, ,, ,, haul in 2nd Gear ... ... ... ... | 410 ,, | 130 ,, | 75 ,, |
| ,, ,, ,, ,, ,, 3rd Gear ... ... ... ... | 260 ,, | 80 ,, | 45 ,, |
| ,, ,, ,, ,, ,, 4th Gear ... ... ... ... | 165 ,, | 45 ,, | 20 ,, |

Loads hauled are based on 18 lbs./ton Starting Resistance and 12 lbs./ton Running Resistance
*Code Word—***BRAND**

# THE HUNSLET ENGINE CO. LTD *Engineers* LEEDS ENGLAND

## 0-4-0 TYPE

# 22 H.P. "HUNSLET" DIESEL LOCOMOTIVE

### FOR UNDERGROUND WORKING

| | |
|---|---|
| Gauge of Railway (can be modified to suit requirements) ... ... ... | 1 ft. 6 in. |
| Dia. of Coupled Wheels ... ... ... ... ... ... ... ... | 1 ft. 4 in. |
| Wheelbase ... ... ... ... ... ... ... ... ... | 2 ft. 0 in. |
| Height Overall ... ... ... ... ... ... ... ... | 4 ft. 1 in. |
| Width Overall ... ... ... ... ... ... ... ... | 3 ft. 3 in. |
| Length over Buffer Beams ... ... ... ... ... ... ... | 8 ft. 0 in. |
| Maximum Power and Speed of Engine ... ... ... ... ... | 22 b.h.p. at 1,300 r.p.m. |
| Maximum Speed in either direction ... ... ... ... ... | 5½ m.p.h. |
| Fuel Capacity ... ... ... ... ... ... ... ... | 7 galls. |
| Weight in Working Order ... ... ... ... ... ... | 3 tons |
| Maximum Axle Load ... ... ... ... ... ... ... | 1 ton 16 cwts. |
| Maximum Tractive Effort ... ... ... ... ... ... | 1,270 lbs. |
| Ratio, Adhesive Weight ÷ Tractive Effort ... ... ... ... ... | 5.3 to 1 |
| Minimum Radius of Curve Engine will traverse without train ... ... | 15 ft. |
| Weight per Yard of Lightest Rail advisable ... ... ... ... | 12 lbs. |
| Load Engine will start and haul on Level ... ... ... ... | 67 tons |
| „ „ „ „ „ „ up Incline of 1 in 100 ... ... ... ... | 28 tons |
| „ „ „ „ „ „ „ „ „ 1 in 50 ... ... ... ... | 18 tons |

Loads hauled are based on a Starting Resistance of 18 lbs. per ton.

*Code Word—***PITPO**

# APPENDIX

This appendix identifies and gives key details of the particular locomotives illustrated on the catalogue pages. After the takeover of the Kerr Stuart and Avonside ranges of locomotives in 1930 and 1935 respectively catalogue sheets were produced of certain of their locomotive designs that Hunslet particularly wished to perpetuate and examples of each have been included within this publication, denoted by KS (Kerr Stuart) and AE respectively.

| Page No. | Works No. | Order No. | CODE | NAME | CUSTOMER | DESPATCHED |
|---|---|---|---|---|---|---|
| 3 | 206 | 3750 | BEDERT | BEDDGELERT | N. Wales Narrow Gauge Rly. Co. | 26.7.78 |
| 4 | 285 | 6000 | MURTA | GUAHISTLA | C. deMurietta & Co. | 24.4.82 |
| 5 | 328 | 6950 | CHAMP | CHAMPERICO | Megaw & Norton | 14.12.83 |
| 6 | 332 | 7000 | HELVA | HUELVA | Richardson & Co., Spain | 18.1.84 |
| 7 | 384 | 8420 | SANTAL | SANTA LUCIA | A.Damaret, Manila | 6.11.85 |
| 8 | 500 | 11760 | ABEJA | - | J. E. A. M. Clark Co. | 11.9.89 |
| 9 | 527 | 12920 | RAFLA | No. 3 | Rafaela Vila, Josefina for TransAndine Rly. | 15.12.90 |
| 10 | 642 | 18170 | DRYBRO | PIONEER | Drysdale Bros., Queensland | 27 01.96 |
| 11 | 659 | 19000 | CARBO | CARBONERAS | Compania Minera & Sierra, Spain | 16.12.96 |
| 12 | 741 | 23400 | HONKON | P.L.& Co. No. 3 | Punchard, Lowther & Co. Ltd. Hong Kong Naval Harbour | 11.3.01 |
| 13 | 783 | 24870 | NALON | NALON No. 21 | J. R. Banks, Spain | 2.12.02 |
| 14 | 806 | 25500 | BOWES | - | Bowes, Scott & Western, Sarawak | 7.2.03 |
| 15 | 431 | 9900 | LARTI | No. 1 | Lartigue Rly. Constrn. Co. for Listowel & Ballybunion Rly., Ireland | 10.10.87 |
| 16 | 812 | 25790 | SERAL | SLGR 11 | Crown Agents, Sierra Leone | 26.8.03 |
| 17 | 840 | 26700 | BASAT | BASIRHAT | T. A. Martin Co., Baraset-Basirhat Rly., India | 24.3.04 |
| 18 | 858 | 27450 | MARJ | MARJORIE | S.Wales Cement & Lime Co., Penarth | 24.11.04 |
| 19 | 865 | 27640 | MASHA | LEEDS No.1 | Leeds City Council, Masham | 24.1.05 |
| 20 | 893 | 28640 | NATGOV | No. 2 | Natal Government Rlys. | 9.3.06 |
| 21 | 904 | 28980 | EVA | EVA HAR No. 17 | Howrah-Amtah Rly., India | 29.9.06 |
| 22 | 934 | 29770 | JUMNA | JUMNA No. 7 | Shadara Rly., India | 10.10.07 |
| 23 | 963 | 30470 | DIANA | DIANA No. 146 | Antafogasta(Chile) & Bolivia Rly. Co. | 23.5.08 |
| 24 | 980 | 31100 | CENCHU | No. 21 | Central Rly. of Chubut, Argentina | 18.8.08 |
| 25 | 992 | 31570 | GROBI | NONUS | Groby Granite Co., Leicester | 18.6.09 |
| 26 | 1009 | 31850 | BENG | - | Indian Iron & Steel Co. | 31.10.09 |

| Page No. | Works No. | Order No. | CODE | NAME | CUSTOMER | DESPATCHED |
|---|---|---|---|---|---|---|
| 27 | 1028 | 32320 | MICRO | MICROBE NO. 1 | Leeds Corpn. Sewage Works | 11.5.10 |
| 28 | 1031 | 32400 | ARRAS | CONSTRUCTION III | Arrah Sasaram Rly., India | 7.5.10 |
| 29 | 1042 | 32560 | FORTU | FORTUNA | Thompson & Hunter, Trinidad | 25.7.10 |
| 30 | 1069 | 33130 | KYSTIM | No. 8 | Kyshtim Corpn., Russia | 14.2.11 |
| 31 | 1099 | 34190 | JOHOR | - | Public Works Dept., Johore | 3.10.12 |
| 32 | 1127 | 34890 | BOLIV | No. 7 | Bolivar Rly. Co., S. America | 31.10.13 |
| 33 | 1128 | 34910 | BRIHO | No. 4 | Crown Agents - Br. Honduras Rly. | 30.4.13 |
| 34 | 1148 | 35520 | SANMAR | No. 18 | Santa Marta Rly., Colombia | 7.3.14 |
| 35 | 1187 | 36360 | BODRY | - | Eng. Supply Co., Australia | 9.6.15 |
| 36 | 1190 | 36420 | SANLU | No. 3 | St. Lucia Sugar Co., Natal | 21.9.15 |
| 37 | 1198 | 36560 | WARIL | - | War Office,Deptford | 3.6.16 |
| 38 | 1205 | 36930 | SHADA | No. 9 - GANGES | Shadara Rly., India | 24.1.21 |
| 39 | 1216 | 37400 | WAROFF | 304 | War Office, France | 16.8.16 |
| 40 | 1428 | 40820 | HAMIL | HAMILTON | Preston Corpn. Waterworks | 29.4.22 |
| 41 | 1430 | 40830 | DINOR | No. 2 | T. Lloyd Williams, Dinorwic | 11.8.22 |
| 42 | 1432 | 40880 | TYMON | 3 ENNISTYMON | West Clare Rly. | 10.10.22 |
| 43 | 1436 | 41030 | STOCS | STOCKS | Fylde Water Board | 24.10.22 |
| 44 | 1481 | 41820 | MIRO | WLADINIRO | Anthy. Gibbs & Son, Chile | 10.9.24 |
| 45 | 1484 | 41940 | SNTMA | 24 | Santa Marta Rly., Colombia | 3.2.25 |
| 46 | 1502 | 42340 | BENAG | 06 | Bengal Nagpur Rly., for Raipur-Dhamatry, India | 22.1.26 |
| 47 | 1679 | 45160 | KBENG | - | Bengal-Nagpur Rly., India | 22.5.31 |
| 48 | 1871 | 48300 | AFZEB | - | Zebedelia Estates, S. Africa | 26.6.37 |
| 49 | 3399 | 54400 | SLEON | S.L.R. 82 | Crown Agents, S. Leone Rly | 24.6.47 |
| 50 | 3871 | 3871 | NALTA | MACBETH | Natal Estates, S. Africa | 29.7.57 |
| 51 | 3873 | 3873 | DOLPH | - | Dholpur Rly. | 29.7.59 |
| 52 | 3875 | 3875 | NEPAL | - | Nepal Jaynagar-Janakpur Rly. | 29.8.62 |
| 53 | (KS)4063 | K4063 | DAWIN | DARWIN | Durant, Radford & Co., for Illovo Sugar Co., Natal | 7.1.24 |
| 54 | (KS)4193 | K4193 | MATRY | MATARY | Carlos Lyra & CIA, Maceio, Brazil | 3.9.27 |
| 55 | (AE)2059 | A10400 | AFOUR | - | Natal Estates | 1931 |
| 56 | (AE)2065 | A11840 | ANHEJ | - | Reynolds Bros., S Africa | 1933 |
| 57 | (AE)2070 | A13440 | ANDIE | - | Doornkop Sugar Estates, Natal | 1935 |
| 58 | 1722 | 47080 | ARTIC | ALBERT | Royal Arsenal, Woolwich, London | 1934 |
| 59 | 4060 | - | - | - | NCB, Pithouse Colliery | 28.9.50 |
| 60 | 4755 | - | - | - | NCB, E. Midlands Divn., Bestwood Colliery | 9.8.54 |